emerge 16

ABOUT *emerge*

In its sixteenth year, *emerge* is an annual publication produced by students, faculty, and industry guests of the Writer's Studio. Students are assigned to teams and, over a four-month period, work with the publisher, editors, designers, our printer, and local booksellers to produce, market, and sell this anthology.

ABOUT THE WRITER'S STUDIO

The Writer's Studio is an award-winning creative writing program at Simon Fraser University that provides writers with mentoring, classroom instruction, and hands-on book publishing experience. Over the course of a year, new writers work with their mentor alongside a community of writers, exploring and developing their writing through regular manuscript workshops and readings. Many of our alumni have become successful authors, and have gone on to careers in the publishing industry.

The Writer's Studio 2016 mentors:
JJ Lee—*Narrative Non-Fiction*
Hiromi Goto—*Speculative Fiction and Writing for Young Adults*
Meredith Quartermain—*Poetry and Lyric Prose*
Kevin Chong—*Fiction*

The Writer's Studio Online 2015–2016 mentors:
Claudia Cornwall—*Narrative Non-Fiction*
Eileen Cook—*Speculative Fiction and Writing for Young Adults*
Fiona Tinwei-Lam—*Poetry and Lyric Prose*
June Hutton—*Fiction*

sfu.ca/write

emerge 16
THE WRITER'S STUDIO ANTHOLOGY

Raoul Fernandes
Foreword

CREATIVE WRITING
AT SFU CONTINUING STUDIES

SFU PUBLICATIONS

Simon Fraser University, Vancouver, B.C.

Cover Design: Amanda Regan
Cover Illustration: Akem
Typesetting and Interior Design: Solo Corps Creative
Printing: Burroughs Printing Ltd.

Printed in Canada

LIBRARY AND ARCHIVES CANADA CATALOGUING IN PUBLICATION

emerge 16: The Writer's Studio anthology /
Foreword by Raoul Fernandes

ISSN 1925-8267
ISBN 978-1-77287-007-7 (paperback)
ISBN 978-1-77287-008-4 (ebook)

A cataloging record for this publication is available
from Library and Archives Canada.

Creative Writing | SFU Continuing Studies
Simon Fraser University
515 West Hastings Street
Vancouver, B.C., Canada, V6B 5K3
sfu.ca/write

SFU Publications
1300 West Mall Centre
8888 University Drive
Burnaby, B.C., Canada, V5A 1S6

To the TWS community, a generous and supportive group that celebrates inspiration, growth, and success together.

"So, artist, you too from the deeps of your soul …
let your roots creep forth, gaining strength."

—Emily Carr

Contents

POETRY AND LYRIC PROSE

FICTION

~

Foreword

In the brief moment before a writer touches a pen to paper or lays their fingertips on a keyboard, there is often something to reckon with—a mirror, a ghost, a little spider of doubt—something they have to face, just to begin. This requires a summoning of courage, an elusive fearlessness that must be called upon frequently at every stage, from first word to final draft.

It is heartening to see all the writers in this anthology show such bravery and risk-taking. Sometimes it's the courage to have a character commit a tragic irreversible act with a gun in a forest. Or the mindfulness to construct a world with meddlesome fairies that still feels human and complex. Or the emotional vulnerability of mourning a loved one while accepting the simultaneous presence of joy. Even asking a simple question in a prose poem—*is my blue your blue?*—can be a startling move. When the writer occasionally falters or stumbles, as all dedicated writers do and must, one can still sense the precipice their consciousness leapt towards, and can't help applaud that leap.

Prior to my own experience at the Writer's Studio in 2009, I was dedicated to my poetry, but adrift—unconnected to a local writing community and hardly sending out poems. Then I found myself in rooms with people of many different backgrounds and ages who were all passionate about this ancient art of putting words on paper. I felt lit up. My generous and perceptive mentor helped me deepen my connection to my work and understand it in a larger context. Through the hours of workshops I became a better writer, but I'm most grateful for the skills I cultivated to be a more attentive and curious reader. I learned the responsibility of deeply listening for the beating heart at the centre of every poem, story, or memoir. And then we developed the skills in relating our experience to each other with lucidity and careful scrutiny. It was always a profound interaction.

The writers you will meet here in this anthology will go on many different trajectories. Some might get their work in journals and magazines, publish books, win awards. Some might continue studying, eventually mentor others. Some might try their new poems at open mics or simply pass a story on to a relative or friend and say, *hey, I wrote this for you*. Or just, *I wrote this*. Wherever they go, this experience they've shared in the Writer's Studio means they have a toolkit for their journey and the foundations of a community that will grow and weave into other communities. It will ensure that in their solitary act of writing, they are not alone. Nor are you, holding this lively chorus of voices in your hands. Welcome.

—*Raoul Fernandes*, Vancouver, 2016

Non-fiction

Elaine Cross

Bodies in Motion
A CONDENSED VERSION

Heat and convulsions washed over her. The heaving slowed, then stopped. She became aware of things beyond her own body: the smell of the toilet, the cold porcelain tile under bare knees. She waited a moment to make sure nothing more would come, and then rose on still-shaky legs.

Neither Rob nor the cats were up yet, so she wandered into the living room. It had the look of a room that had been heavily partied in the night before. Luckily for her, there were no leftover guests, so she gingerly sat down on the sofa and cleared bottles and glasses from the large coffee table so she could put her feet up. She had the dubious honour of being lady of the house, presiding over this launch pad for all the city offered. Most weekends saw this as the gathering place before the night began, and the roosting place for those determined to see the night to its end.

Though this was her scene, she was beginning to lose her taste for it. Being part of a roving band of wild things—exploring the city, sharing art, dancing like maniacs, imbibing every substance, playing on beaches, laughing hysterically—had been her homecoming after a decade away. Landing back in the west, she had felt like an Amish kid gone rogue. She'd wanted to devour every experience. Lately though, it had come to seem self-indulgent.

She lay down on the couch, and her head came to rest on a hoodie that had been discarded the night before. Inhaling deeply, she brought its owner to her mind's eye. As her thoughts strayed to the night before—stolen looks of hunger, the odd trail of fingers across skin, the magnet-like pull between them, so that each movement was plotted as a point in relation to each other—she had to tuck her robe between her legs to quiet the pulsing. She wanted *him* more than anything, and yet she loved her husband and believed in their marriage. Luckily, her "other man" was honourable in most respects. She wasn't sure she would have been able to resist temptation otherwise, but as much as *he* always hung close, gazing and even touching briefly when opportunity arose, *he* also loved Rob so the three of them existed in this strange orbit.

The sun had reached its mid-morning point, reflecting off glass skyscrapers at the perfect angle to glint in her eyes. She suddenly felt nausea pass over her again, and debated whether she was ready to begin the day. Shuffling back into the dark bedroom, where heavy blinds kept out any attempt at natural light, she shoved aside a cat or two and sidled her length against his. Smooth skin, elegant limbs, curly dark hair, and the scent of home: his very bigness drained every knot and worry out of her as she shucked her robe to press her bare body against him. He moaned softly in his sleep, barely registering her presence before descending into the depths again.

⌒

"Babe, can you bring me some water?" She was relaxing in the tub after work, a luxury usually reserved for a weekend. After days of not feeling right, she thought a bath might help. He sauntered in and set her glass on a small table beside the deep, claw-foot tub. "Stay with me a minute, would you?" she implored. He closed the toilet lid and sat down, glancing at her glistening wet body.

"I bought a test, just in case," she said, without quite catching his eye.

Rob looked at her. "Jesus, it can't be that," he said softly. She saw fear in his eyes, mixed with something else. They were both in their mid-thirties, an age when many might consider starting a family, but in their circle, kids were considered distasteful, irresponsible. *He* in particular believed so ardently in voluntary human extinction, that *he'd* had a vasectomy years ago.

"Well, it probably isn't that. God knows we've been doing this long enough that if that was going to happen it would've happened already," she babbled to cover her slight disappointment at his reaction. "I'll do the test, we'll find out it's not that, and I'll go see a doctor tomorrow."

He said nothing, lost in his own thoughts, and after a moment stood up. "I'm going to get dinner ready. Will you be ready to eat in a half hour or so?"

"Yep, I'll finish up and be out in a few minutes."

She finished her bath and got out, all the while studiously avoiding the little cardboard box on the old radio that served as a vanity. Suddenly with resolve, she downed her water and grabbed the box. After perusing the instructions, she peed and waited. She wondered momentarily what she hoped the result would be. If it were positive, it meant there wasn't anything seriously wrong with her. How would he take it, though?

A few minutes passed and she examined the test. There was a distinct cross. She looked at the instructions again. A definite positive. She sat still, feeling nothing. No sinking, no jubilation, just a slight empty feeling. Pulling on her robe, she tucked the test into her pocket.

The coffee table that served as their dinner table was neatly set. She sat down, and put the test on the table without comment. Rob looked at her but could discern nothing from her face as she began eating. He looked at the test, read through the instructions, looked at the test again.

"It can't be positive. I don't believe it." He read the instructions again, as suddenly misunderstanding his mother tongue was more plausible and welcome than the truth conveyed by those two intersecting lines.

"I think it says what it says," she replied, quietly.

"It's got to be a mistake. I think you should go to the doctor tomorrow and find out what's really wrong."

Silence descended. After a while of staring at nothing, he finally got up, mumbled something about going for a walk, put on his coat and left. She let him go, feeling a vague sensation of motion-sickness.

⌒

It was Friday evening, the beginning of the weekend, and they were both tidying up. Brian, their neighbour, was already positioned on the deck, having a drink. She and Rob worked in coordinated fashion, and their flow had a certain grace to it. Though they didn't talk, they were in perfect sync.

As the evening wore on, more people arrived, including *him*. Despite herself, her yearning flowed out to *him*, like a tendril looking for foothold. It was a beautiful May evening, so everyone collected on the deck, enjoying the summery weather. She was in the hammock, strung from one end of the tiny deck to the other, with all other seats positioned around the edge. With a single person in it, the hammock had a tendency to close over on top, creating something of a cocoon, and she hung there in pupal state.

"Did anybody see that video with the guy and the double rainbow?"

"Oh yeah, I saw that. Hilarious! I wonder what he's on."

"I didn't see it. What was it about?"

"Oh, just this guy out in California or wherever, who's on mushrooms or something, freaking out over a complete double rainbow."

"You say it like a complete double rainbow is an ordinary thing."

"Well, I might get that excited about some things, but I don't think a rainbow is going to be one of them."

"That's the extraordinary thing about it! That someone could feel such intense joy over an atmospheric event. It's cool!"

"Cool, if you're wasted on mushrooms I guess."

Through the conversation, she lay quietly, taking it all in and not contributing. She was enjoying the ebb and flow, lying there in perfect stillness, arms crossed over her chest like someone in a coffin.

"Did you read that the new projection for human population is pegged at almost ten billion by 2050?"

"And we're already teetering on the brink of it as we speak. How can the planet possibly support another few billion people?"

"Overpopulation leads inevitably to population crash. Disease will wipe everyone out. Either that or we'll wipe ourselves out."

"The breeders are killing this world," *he* said.

Suddenly the hanging effect was no longer soothing, and she rolled out of the hammock, darting for the bathroom which was luckily empty. She made it to the toilet in time, spewed what little was in her stomach, and spent a few minutes recovering before returning. As she stood on the threshold of the deck, many of her guests looked up.

She looked at Rob, whose gaze was locked on her, took a breath, and said, "I'm pregnant."

Complete silence descended over the group.

She could feel *his* gaze searing into her, heating her entire body and making her flush. She finally looked over and their eyes met. There was an imperceptible change. Gravity shifted, and *he* looked away.

Clara Cristofaro
This Bird

I'm in the mall pet store, trying not to breathe. The place stinks of sawdust and urine. Puppies yip from their wire cages and birds chatter and squawk from the back of the store. A clerk stands at the front counter, bored, thumbing through a magazine. He twitches whenever someone sets off the door chime

My three-year-old son doesn't notice the smell or the noise. He plasters his face against a plastic wall and grins at the kittens, tracing his finger up and down. When a kitten comes close to inspect him, he presses his small palm against its paw through the window, like a visitor to jail.

I bring him to the mall for entertainment while his older brother is at school. This place satisfies a preschooler's need for novelty; he can climb on play structures and handle every animal puppet in the toy store. We can sit together in a coffee shop and mimic civilized behavior; I can drink a cup of coffee while he feeds on a muffin, as we watch people shuffle through the corridors of the mall.

A trip to the mall serves a purpose for me, too, a purpose greater than getting out of the house on a rainy day. I come here to hide in plain sight.

Five years into motherhood, I feel dull, like a pair of overused scissors. Sometimes I think fondly of my former self—someone sharp and bright, driven and creative. I wonder if motherhood necessarily dulls us, so we don't cut our children. I'm not a bad mother, but I'm not like the others either. I meet them in playgrounds and at preschool, the women who parent without effort, delighting in their children. They are comfortable in their parent skin, competent in a way I envy.

In my late thirties, I am a teenager again, with her hood up, hiding from the world while she makes the transformation from one state to the next. I walk through my days as a version of myself I don't much like or understand. The mall is a good place to be in between; I can be anonymous here, invisible, yet still a participant in the world.

The pet store is almost always empty, except for the occasional catnip shopper. Animals in cages don't attract groups of parents and kids the way books and toys do. There is no risk of being engaged in conversation. The pet store plays no music and does nothing to make people want to stay. We do stay, though, because this is a place I can stop and rest, a moment of silence in my day. I can pretend I am alone while my son occupies himself with the animals, tripping with happiness from hamster to lizard.

I check the time on my phone. "Ten more minutes," I say. My son doesn't look up. He has buried his hands in a bin of rubber dog toys. Soon he'll discover how satisfying it is to squeak them, and our time in this store will be up.

I'm moving to the back of the store, just past the clucking budgies, when I look up and see this bird. He is a tropical sort of bird, his feathers coloured like a box of good pencil crayons. He is in a cage by himself, his head tilted to one side, and he is staring at me.

I don't want an overpriced, overbred puppy. I don't want a kitten, or a hamster, or a fish. But from the moment our eyes meet, I do want this bird.

He has long, black claws. His head is as green as a rainforest. His eyes are small, shiny beads. The feathers on his head stand up when I say hello. He is listening to me. He cocks his head and his feathers lie down. I tell him I like his feathers, that he seems like a very nice bird, very pretty. He claws his way down the bars of the cage and moves closer to me. I want this bird.

I want to startle and thrill the store clerk. "Take my credit card and

I will take this bird, damn the expense. Please fill a bag with food, and can you tell me how to take him on an escalator? And how to explain my silver sedan when he is used to first, the jungle, and then, a bag over his head, and then, a cage in this pet shop?"

I look at the bird's eyes and we make conversation. He presses his body against his cage and I keep my hands clenched in my pockets.

I don't want to pet him.

I do want to pet him.

I don't want him to be a pet, but I do want to touch his tiny heart through his warm feathers and let him know there are good humans, that I am one.

Oh bird, I wish I had a thousand dollars to buy you, take you to a field, and watch as you beat your wings hard against the air and lift yourself up into the clouds. I wish I could free you.

And bird, I wish I could be sure that after I'd spent the thousand dollars I wouldn't take you home for a little while. Just to keep you on my arm in the kitchen, stroke your feathers, and make like I'd saved you.

I wish I wasn't able to see myself picking out a cage and some seed, to make my own pretty zoo with you, my rainbow bird. Before long, I fear I'd have another bird to keep you company. The kids would try to teach you tricks. They'd bring their friends over and yell pirate and parrot things at you through the bars. That one mean friend would tease you and I'd have to speak firmly to him.

The store has fallen away. We're connected, this bird and I; he sees me and seems to take me in without any of the judgement I feel from humans, or from myself. I'm bathing in it, glowing under his gaze. I need this.

Then he turns away and I'm in the dark again.

I close my eyes. I can still see his feathers, his long claws. I see him seeing me, the old me, the whole me. My former self, my current self, the messy merging of the two; I see it all. I don't have to hide until I'm perfectly formed. I have been seen, and all of me is already here.

This bird and I have recognized each other. I know what I see in him: a reflection of my former self, someone colourful and confident. But what could he see in me, a graceless human?

It can only be that I have freedom. My days are within my control and my cage is of my own making. I can leave this store when I want. I can leave this mall. I could even leave my family.

I open my eyes. I turn and find my son nose to nose with a puppy behind a glass window, enjoying his own reflection. I reach down and tap him on the shoulder. "Time to go," I say. He folds his fingers into a small sticky fist that I envelop with my hand. I offer to buy him a muffin, and he agrees to leave the store.

I hold the bird in my mind as my son and I walk back through the mall to our car. The bird with his head tilted, his unblinking eye on me. I look ahead as I walk. I am a black and white film washed with colour, a paper doll given breath. The glow of his gaze is off me but I still feel the light he cast. I am visible, imperfect, free.

Amelia Teresa Hirota

Unlikely Love

The player behind me dives to make a beautiful pass. The setter sends the worn volleyball high in the air. I jump, smack the ball hard and snap my wrist for maximum topspin. The ball pounds the sand amongst the all-male team and the audience of Malay men on motorbikes erupts into cheers and laughter. I high-five my generous setter, who beams a mouth full of white teeth. We continue playing until the wailing call to prayer comes from the village mosque. Magrib is the fourth of five daily prayers for Muslims and coincides with sunset. In Malaysia, Magrib prayers signal the time to go indoors, much like the streetlights coming on cleared out my childhood street at dinner. All of the volleyball players and the spectators quickly jump on their motorbikes to return home for baths and prayers.

Unlike my fellow Occidental College graduates in 1988, who leave Los Angeles for Wall Street, medical school or law school, I buy a one-way ticket to Hong Kong. After Hong Kong, I travel to China, Indonesia, Australia, and Singapore before arriving in Malaysia. I only intend to spend a few days here before rushing off to the banana pancake trail in Thailand, made famous by Lonely Planet's ubiquitous yellow bible, *Southeast Asia on a Shoestring*. However, my host in Kuala Lumpur convinces me to visit a quaint fishing village on the east coast of Malaysia.

Cherating Village, a brand new destination on the backpacker's circuit, has accommodation at Mak De's Guesthouse or Mak Long Te's Guesthouse. Mak means mother in the Malay language and both businesses are run by strong matriarchs. Each property offers a traditional wooden bungalow, breakfast and dinner for three dollars. I choose

Mak De's next to the volleyball court. Both places have about twenty travelers staying there, which means forty young backpackers and one hundred Malays in this tiny seaside village. The locals know you by name after a couple of days.

Dinner at Mak De's is a spicy Malaysian pumpkin-coconut curry with fluffy white rice. Drink options include tea, coffee, or chocolate Milo with sweetened condensed milk. All of the backpackers hang out after dinner to chat or play cards over hot Milos. I love swapping travel stories with my tribe of like-minded nomads. Eventually travelers drift off to their bungalows or wander down to the beach.

After dinner I see the setter from the volleyball game lingering by the dining room door, looking uncomfortable and nervous. I walk over and he puts out his hand, "Hi, my name's Amie, like the Emmy Awards."

"I'm Teresa. Thanks for the awesome game today." We shake hands and his right hand touches his chest. I later learn that Malays touch their chest after shaking hands to symbolize bringing the friendship to their heart.

Amie asks, "Do you want to come down to the beach? A group of us are having a bonfire tonight."

Never one to miss a party, I answer, "Sure. Lead the way." Although I enjoy hanging out with locals when traveling, I am cautious of starting a romantic relationship. I naively believe that Amie and I can just be friends.

The bright moon illuminates the water as we slosh through the sandy marsh that separates the guest house from the stunning South China Sea. When we arrive at the beach, a circle of travelers and Malay men are sitting around a fire and a handsome Malay guy is playing the guitar. His name is Daniya and he speaks English with a Manchester accent. He absorbed his English girlfriend's accent like a sponge. Daniya plays old classics, new pop songs, and contemporary Malay love ballads.

The Malay love song, "Isabella," is wildly famous. Even as a traveler I recognize the melody from markets and buses. The rock group, Search, wrote "Isabella" about two young lovers destined to always be apart because of their different cultures. Malaysia has seventeen million people with the majority Malays, followed by Chinese and then Indians. Not only do their ethnicities differ, but their religions, as well. Malaysians know unrequited love. Intermarriage between races and across religions is rare.

When Daniya strums "Isabella," all the young Malay men join in and sing their hearts out. "Isabella" is everyone's song in Cherating. Tourism is new in Malaysia, but eventually Cherating will be the setting for many "Isabella" stories. Young women from all over the world come to Malaysia and stay on in Cherating because of the charming Malay men and the sweet village life.

With Isabella's haunting tune in our ears, Amie holds my hand and walks me back to my room. In the shadows of the seaside coconut grove, Amie tries to kiss me. I find it hard to think logically after a romantic fireside evening filled with enchanting Malay love songs, but I stop Amie. "I'm sorry, but I really don't want to have a boyfriend for just a couple of days. Can't we just be friends?"

Amie is persuasive, "But you are so beautiful. Why can't we just enjoy the time you are here? I really like you and want to be with you."

My intent weakens and I draw the line at sex in my mind. "Okay, we can kiss, but nothing more." He kisses me with a gentle passion. Just as we connected on the volleyball court, our souls merge in that kiss. Amie's eyes are wide open like he's never watched a kiss in a movie.

My resolve not to have sex with Amie eventually breaks down and my brief stopover in Cherating grows to six weeks. I'm falling in love with this quiet, observant man. Amie has jet black hair, crazy Italian eyebrows, kind eyes, a gorgeous smile and a Tom Selleck moustache. We're the same height at 5'6" and both of us would give our left pinky finger for just two more inches of height. We both love playing sports and are jealous of our taller friends, who do little with their extra height.

I really like playing volleyball with Amie. He is a great all-around player, who gives it his all every game. When he has the chance, he sets me, so I can spike. He really enjoys watching a woman pound the ball on a team of men. I later learn that I have found the rare Malay feminist in this little Muslim village.

In an intimate moment I ask, "How many children do you want to have?"

"I'd like thirteen daughters, so I can have my own all-female football team in Malaysia. What about you?"

"To be honest, I'm just focused on not getting pregnant. I do like the idea of adopting in the future. I'm only twenty-three and I don't want to get married before I'm thirty." We realize that the bridge between our cultures hasn't been built yet so we vow to just enjoy the time we have together.

My days start with roti canai for breakfast. Roti canai is a dough that is stretched to transparent thinness and then folded and fried on a hot griddle. The tissue layers weave alternating crispy and gooey bits which I tear with my hands and dip in curry or dahl sauce. The savory roti canai is complemented by the sweet toffee-like kopi susu (coffee with sweetened condensed milk). I stuff myself daily with roti canai, as do the other budget travelers.

I love Malaysian food, but I'm not happy that I've gained fifteen pounds. I barely dodged the bulimic bullet in college after dating a guy that made me feel guilty for eating a second piece of pizza. In contrast, Amie loves to feed me. "Eat more curry, honey. Do you want more rice?"

I try to refuse. "No, I've eaten too much already. I'm getting fat with this yummy Malaysian food."

"You're not fat at all. I love your body." Amie's sincerity is touching and I wrap myself in his unconditional love.

One balmy night we decide to hike over the hill to the private beach and camp out. The moon is huge as it hangs over the South China Sea. I have some bad news for Amie. "I'm running out of money, so I'm going to Japan to teach English next week."

"Will you come back to Cherating after Japan?"

"I'm not sure, but I promise to send you weekly aerogrammes from Japan." We're both crying and we stay up all night pledging our love to each other.

After a beautiful farewell party on the beach the next week, Daniya drives us to Kuantan, where we have a horrible goodbye at the dusty bus station. I hug Amie in spite of the women in hijab staring at us. "I wish I didn't have to leave. I'm going to miss you so much."

"I'll miss you too. I promise to write and tell you what's happening in Cherating. Please come back to me."

I board the bus for Thailand, where I can buy professional clothes for work and catch a cheap flight to Tokyo. It's six hours to the border and then an overnight train to Bangkok. I cry all the way to Bangkok.

The crazy city of Bangkok and the backpacker scene on Khao San Road cheer me up and welcome me back to the traveler's world. The intoxicating smell of Bangkok streets would be described by a sommelier as a humid bouquet of flowers, spices, exhaust, and open sewage. As I walk along the Chao Praya river, I listen to Malay love songs on my Walkman. My heart is breaking for this beautiful Malay man. My heart savors Amie's genuine love, but my brain suspects we may be another "Isabella" story. My idyllic time in Cherating with Amie will haunt me for many years.

Ben Ross

The Greatest

AN EXCERPT

"I am the Greatest Surgeon in the World!"

My wife looked up from her seafood fettuccini with a slightly annoyed look.

"What?"

Her look made me less confident and I decided to rephrase my statement.

"I think that I may be the Greatest Surgeon in the World."

"What are you talking about, are you drunk?"

"Maybe a little."

I was in my fourth year of a five-year Surgical Residency in Halifax, Nova Scotia and things were going well. Very well. I had become proficient at performing a complex surgical procedure used to treat Esophageal Cancer known as a Transhiatal Esophagectomy. The most dreaded complication of this procedure was an anastomotic leak or "breakdown in the connection or suture line." This was often fatal. The national average for this complication was 25 to 30%. Mine was zero. That's right, zero for ten. So after draining my third glass of expensive red wine at our favourite restaurant I had decided to inform my wife who she was really married to.

"No, listen to me, I have performed ten Esophagectomies on this rotation so far and there have been no leaks, or major complications." I felt somewhat reassured by this truthful statement and refilled my wine glass deciding to press ahead. Ha! I thought, my wife ain't so bad. Therefore, I think that I am the "Greatest Surgeon in the World". I thought about veering off onto a drunken Descarte philosophical spin but thankfully did not.

"That is ridiculous, you are talking like a moron. Did you ask the Chief Resident if you could have our anniversary night off?"

Of course I had not asked my Chief Resident for time off. I would not have asked for time off if both of my parents had died in a fiery plane crash. I decided to stay on the offensive and not show any signs of weakness.

⌒

"Dad, open the door, it's our turn to watch TV."

"Just a minute." I had locked the door to the den because I had wanted to watch the show alone, free to release my convulsive grief without judgement or family concern. I wiped the tears off my face with my sleeve and paused the show. I had stumbled across a Netflix documentary titled "I am Ali." It had brought back a memory of dinner with my wife during Residency Training. A time when I was golden, invincible, "The Greatest." A time before my diagnosis.

I thought that I knew everything that there was to know about his life but this film took a different approach, using audio tapes and conversations that Ali had had with his family and friends to reveal the man behind the persona. Sure, he was a fantastic boxer, arguably the greatest of all time, but the film allowed us a brief glimpse into the intelligence and sensitivity of the man. He loved his children. He had many of them. He was brave beyond measure. Think about it: here was a black man from Louisville Kentucky, who was willing to stand up for his beliefs, and take on the U.S. Government when he refused to be drafted into the Vietnam War. Obviously there was more to it, Muhammad was dangerous to the establishment. He was wildly popular, articulate and black. What better way to silence him then stick him in the middle of a rice paddy to fight a highly trained enemy on their own soil.

Ali said no. Fuck that. The U.S. Government was behaving like a bully and he was not about to acquiesce. Ali hated bullies in all shapes, sizes, and colours. In fact, he started boxing at age twelve because he was being bullied. They played an interview of Ali's business manager. He said that Ali could have been anything he wanted to be, asking "Could you imagine him with a Harvard Law Degree?"

But life can be cruel and unfortunately Ali, like me, developed Parkinson's. He was undeniably one of the most perfect athletic specimens ever created. He had speed, he had power, he had balance. He was beautiful. A devastatingly handsome man who moved with a fluidity that had never been seen before. And then there was the talk. You could devote an entire book on this subject. He was the undisputed master of trash talk, able to spew a constant stream of hurtful words that would beat his opponents down before they even stepped in the ring. Just ask Joe.

But Parkinsons changed that. What a fucking tragedy. It was devastating. We all wanted to help as we watched him shuffle across the stage to light the Olympic Cauldron in Atlanta. One scene in the movie that really stuck with me was an interview with one of his ex-wives. She obviously still loved him and at one point she started to cry and needed to take a break "I'm sorry," she said, "I was just thinking about his current situation." And there you have it. This disease is a real motherfucker. I read Michael J. Fox's book and he described himself as being lucky for having PD. Lucky? I call bullshit, I'll take me at the top of my game every-time. But there is one thing that might get me through this—humour. But as the disease progresses the humour tends to give way to tragedy. Wasn't that a Shakespearean thing— tragic comedy? Maybe I should reread all that shit.

"You don't believe me? You don't believe that I'm "The Greatest Surgeon in the World?"

"No, of course not, that is a ridiculous statement."

"Well how do you know it's not true?"

"Because if it were true, you would be training at Harvard."

Hmmmm, valid argument but I knew that there was a fault in her logic. The prestige of a University can often instill a sense of entitlement in Residents, and this decreases their desire to constantly improve their skills by participating in as many surgical cases as possible.

"Let's talk about something else," she said with increasing irritation.

But I just wouldn't let it go.

"Did you ever think that you would be married to the Greatest Surgeon in the World?"

"Holy fuck!"

Oh oh, I've pushed it too far. She stood up and pushed her chair back suddenly.

"I'm outta here!" Before I could react she had grabbed her coat and was out the door. I was a little stunned but not really. I have always had a tendency to push people away when they get close to me. The waiter came by to enquire as to what had happened? I felt my cheeks flush as I noticed that some couples at adjacent tables were smirking. Yeah laugh it up, but you might need me one day, I thought. I told the waiter what had happened and without missing a beat he asked "Perhaps the Greatest Surgeon in the world would like a doggy bag?" I felt myself sinking back to earth and heard myself say "Yes, yes he would." A wry smile spread across his face. I grinned, waited for the leftovers, and then waved goodbye as I walked out the door. It was snowing and I remember thinking to myself, why do I always end up alone?

Lindsay Beckett

The Distance Between Us

My daughter phones from Toronto. I can tell from her voice that she's been crying but we begin with our usual polite small talk.

"Hi, Mum, how's it going?"

"Fine honey, how about you?"

We speak carefully to each other. Knowing that the wrong word or inflection of voice can set us off on one of our fights. We tiptoe around each other and speak as if to a distant relative.

"I just got back from a walk on the beach," I tell her. "You wouldn't believe all the seals out in the bay. There must be hundreds of them."

The seals had been circling around near the shore, their sleek black heads popping up as they peered at each other above the swells.

I'm currently on a sabbatical from my job in Victoria. I've been staying at our cabin on Rathtrevor Beach, taking a break from my hospital job and trying to write. I'd gone out early for my usual morning walk and had seen the seals through the trees as I'd walked along the wooded trail that runs along the park near our cabin.

"They look like they're having a board meeting." I'd called out to a bearded man in a brown plaid jacket walking past me on the beach. "The herring should be running soon," he told me, "the seals are out there waiting for dinner." I nod as I remembered hearing on the radio just that morning that all the fishing boats were sitting at the dock in Comox waiting for the herring to run. They were interviewing the skipper from one of the boats who'd said they were predicting a pretty good herring run this year.

But how do the seals know this, I wonder silently to his departing back. They don't have radios or computers. Do they communicate with some form of underwater email?

I tell my daughter this little anecdote in an attempt to lift her mood, but she is not amused at her mother's flights of fancy. Her voice is despondent as she says: "It's twenty below zero here, minus forty with the wind-chill factor. It's so frickin' freezing we can't even go outside." Her voice sounds flat and nasally.

"And are you sick?" I ask her. "You sound funny."

"Yeah I've had a cold, but it's getting better." Her voice falters and she starts to cry.

"Emily, what's wrong?"

"I'm so bored I don't know what to do now I don't have school and dad is being an idiot."

Emily and I had moved to Victoria from Toronto after her dad and I got divorced. Jim had worked hard to maintain a long distance relationship with his only daughter and after high school she'd gone to live with him in Toronto and attend college. But recently she dropped all her courses and was now trying to find full time work.

I struggle to find the words to comfort her. To connect across the three thousand miles that separate Victoria from Toronto, mother from daughter. I want to live up to the myth that I, her mother, can make everything better. But even as I form the words, I know they will bring cold comfort. No matter what platitudes I recite, she will react in anger and disdain. Her voice will drip with the contempt that only a twenty-one-year-old daughter can muster.

If I tell her things will get better, she will answer that I don't know what I'm talking about. If I tell her it's never as bad as it seems at the moment; every cloud has a silver lining, she will answer that I never understand anything. If tell her I understand more than she thinks, for I'm her mother after all, she will say that's the problem: I am her mother and I know zip. Then the gloves will go off.

In the now classic, *My Mother/My Self*, author Nancy Friday writes:

"We are raised to believe that mother love is different from other kinds of love. It is not open to error, doubt or the ambivalence of ordinary affections. This is an illusion."

An illusion Emily sees right through. For to her I am no longer the omniscient mother who knows all and can fix all. The Great Oz had been exposed. At about the age of eleven she pulled back the curtain and saw me madly flipping the dials and switches. She revealed me for who I am; just an ordinary woman offering oatmeal cookies, and love, with a dash of experience.

Now when I offer advice, she construes it as criticism and interference. She will have to make mistakes and suffer disappointments that I cannot protect her from. So I have learned (most of the time) to keep my mouth shut, and to keep my sage advice to myself. Sometimes, I have to press my lips together to keep the words from escaping. I so want to warn her of the perils of losing one's temper in public; of the danger of not wanting anyone to "get away with" slighting you. I want to give her the benefits of my experience, prevent her from making the same mistakes that I did, save her from the hurt. But she does not want to hear.

As I grasp for the words to comfort her, my mind slips back to thirty years ago when I would telephone my mother in Toronto from my basement apartment in the constantly rainy, dreary Vancouver. At the first sound of my voice she would know instantly why I was calling.

"Ah, honey," she'd say. "You always feel like this when it rains. The sun will come out tomorrow and then you'll feel better, and I won't hear from you again for months."

"But you don't understand," I'd say. "You don't know."

But like the seals bobbing in the waves, waiting patiently for the herring to come, she did.

And so I listen as my daughter pours out her grief, and I tell her I love her, and that I know she will figure it out. I give her words of support, but not advice or solutions, for she is now a woman no longer the child I could comfort with a cookie and a hug.

"Yeah, well, I gotta go now, I'm going to the gym." She says this in a tone that tells me I have not helped to dispel her gloom.

We sign off with our ritual, "I love you, Ems."

"I love you too."

I hang up the phone and look out the window. The seals are gone now and all I can see are the vast grey waters of the Pacific Ocean rolling out to meet the sky.

Yaron Sidney Butterfield
From Far and Wide
OUR DRIVE ACROSS CANADA

As we make our way back to the vehicle, my heart starts to sink. The trunk is open and a door ajar. I knew this would eventually happen. As Carsten rushes to the trunk, I think back to seven days ago....

His grey Volkswagen Jetta pulls up on the suburban street in front of my parents' house in Maple Ridge, B.C. A beautiful mid-August morning in 1997, Carsten and I are starting our journey across Canada. I was very excited—what a great character to be spending the next ten or so days driving with. Other than a small trip to Montreal the year before with friends to see my favorite team in one of the last games at the Montreal Forum, I had not been to any other provinces. Quebec City was his ultimate goal for studies while I was going to be flying overseas from New York—my first passport stored safely in my luggage.

☞

Carsten was one of my first roommates while going to Simon Fraser University four years earlier. We lived with two other guys. Dave and Gurdev, in a house in Coquitlam. Dave, who I knew as a teammate on the Track and Field team, invited me to live with them. Carsten and I connected right away as he was also an avid runner. We would often do 10 km runs that ended with going up the steep hill of Thermal Drive before turning off to our place on Park Crescent. Every time we ran that portion, I saw the plaque marking Rick Hansen's tour. If he could go up in a wheelchair, I certainly could without one.

I recall the time Dave, Gurdev and I came home from an evening out to find the front door unlocked and no one home. We were first worried about our stuff and if anything was stolen. Then we were worried about what happened to Carsten until he appeared at the front door in sweat, having just run his own "Man in Motion". We angrily reminded him that the last one out has to lock the door, but his view was that everything is fine.

"No one's going to 'break into' a home where the door is unlocked," he snapped back.

This was a bone of contention between all of us for the remainder of the semester. Another time, I was on my own as Carsten, Dave, and Gurdev had gone out to see a movie. Before getting back to my studies, I thought I would fuel up with a quick dinner of perogies and cottage cheese and then do a run. Carsten and Dave were faster than me and I thought this was a chance to get in some extra training. After the meal, I removed the garbage lid and scraped away what was left in the pan. Then I quickly headed out with my Saucony running shoes, making sure to lock the door. Upon returning, there was a strange smell, like something was burning. I ran to the kitchen and the garbage lid was melting on the oven element surrounded with black smoke—I had left the element on. I quickly removed the lid and stuffed it in the back yard. Over the next few days, questions came up as to where the garbage can lid was.

"Maybe Carsten didn't lock the door again and someone came in and stole it," I said with a smile.

As Carsten gets out of the car, I help manoeuvre his luggage and his sister's precious guitar, so I could fit my suitcases and backpack in the trunk. After giving my parents a hug, we were on our way. Always being the idealist, I was surprised to hear he still had his theory that people really didn't need to lock their doors. Apparently this applied to vehicles too. He felt that lots of crime and theft occur because of the barriers we put up to stop it. It was hard for me to argue, I mean, he was well on his way to completing his Masters in Criminology. So we made a compromise, we'd alternate between locked and unlocked doors at each stop along the way. And thus began our travels across this great, beautiful and stunning country.

Our first stop was in Banff where we set up a campsite and went on a small hike. We were surprised how easy the hikes were in comparison to the guide book. The picture of Moraine Lake on the $20 bill does not do justice to what we saw. The peacefulness didn't last by the time we went to bed however, as we had to listen to someone cranking Bob Marley into the wee hours. Carsten has hated Bob Marley tunes ever since. By early morning, we were off and on our way to Calgary.

After an evening playing pool in Calgary, our next stop was Regina where Carsten had some friends. We continued to switch locking the door or not at each stop. Whenever it was "his turn", I felt a little nervous. However, the stunning horizon underneath the blazin' sky distracted me. Somehow we got lost in the Regina countryside but eventually found our way.

On to Winnipeg where we visited Fort Garry which used to be a Hudson's Bay Company trading post. We enjoyed the simpleness we felt in Winnipeg and ended up staying two nights. To make up time, we decided to drive straight from Winnipeg to Toronto without stopping. Carsten had to be in Quebec City in time to start his studies. As the day turned to night, we traded stories of our days as roommates along with deep philosophical conversations on life. About 2 a.m. somewhere around Thunder Bay, I suddenly wake up to industrial music, and notice Carsten half asleep while driving. Time to switch. Unfortunately, our attempt in the middle of the night to find the Terry Fox memorial was not successful. We probably went right past it. So I drove on with my own thoughts as Carsten slept.

Little did I know that Terry Fox would become a big inspiration to me seven years later. In March 2004, I was diagnosed with a devastating brain cancer—glioblastoma multiforme (GBM). Average survival, even with aggressive treatment, is less than one year. I had to push myself on a daily basis just like Terry. The following year, my twin brother Noam gave me the replica Terry Fox shoes sold to raise money for cancer research. Knowing this hero had run a marathon a day twenty-five years earlier, I thought to myself, I can certainly do it once. So wearing my Terry Fox shoes, I trained over a few months and then ran my first full marathon in Iceland.

A couple years later, on a small road trip, I stopped at Mt. Terry Fox beside Jasper National Park. There were panels of information on his story and looking at this kind of made up for missing his memorial in Thunder Bay. I now wear the replica shoes at every annual Terry Fox Run and as I circle around Stanley Park in Vancouver, I have time to meditate on what he had done. Thinking of powerful moments from his past and mine gave me strength in the present. I had to soldier on—only I knew what must be done.

After driving through the sunrise that reflected over the Great Lakes, Carsten and I finally got to Toronto. We met our old roommate Gurdev, who was now working on a degree in Naturopathic Medicine. We laughed as we shared stories of our time living together. Soon after we made a brief stop in Ottawa giving us the chance to visit the Parliament Buildings and Rideau Hall. I was feeling proud to soak in our Canadian heritage, but I was excited about Montreal.

When we stopped in Montreal, it was "Carsten's turn"—the car doors would be unlocked. After coming back from lunch we noticed the back trunk of the car was ajar and when we opened it, things were ruffled and messed up, and stuff was missing. We had been broken into. Well, not really as the doors were unlocked. My flight from New York was only days away and I had left my passport in a bag in the trunk. We slowly realized that while many things were stolen, including the special guitar and his running shoes, it was all of Carsten's belongings. During the drive, our bags became quite mixed up in the trunk, but all my belongings were still there, including the bag with my passport. Now I felt relieved. I made sure the big smile I felt didn't appear on my face. My point was made. He wanted the doors unlocked. I wanted them locked. For me, thieves were not welcome whereas he was inviting them. I never did tell him that they did actually take one thing of mine, my Sarah McLaughlin CD that was in the player in the front of the car. I made sure not to voice this and followed him to the police station to file a report. Then, when we got back, we had a parking ticket. Carsten, of course, was very upset and just wanted to get out of Montreal.

So we made our way to Quebec City right away. After a quick shopping trip to replace some of Carsten's things, including his underwear, we headed to the old city to stay in a hostel. We met a mutual friend who happened to be there, Lindsay, and we all had a nice poutine dinner. Early the next morning, we parted ways. Carsten would be beginning his studies while I took the train back to Montreal. I thought to myself that now I really could enjoy the city. I took a tour of the new rink my beloved Canadiens were now playing in and visited the artistic district.

The next day I took the train to New York to begin my next adventure. While my luggage was stored in the compartments underneath, I made sure my passport was in my pocket and with a smile, I wondered if Carsten was now locking the doors of his car.

Jacob Enns

The Grieving Ride

Rain streamed down the visor of my helmet and tears streamed down my face as a winding road led me through the mountains. Propelled as much by explosions of grief as by explosions in the twin cylinders of motorcycle, grieving for my uncle led me to the equally twisty road of the loss of my father 12 years prior.

It started, as grief often does, with an unexpected phone call from family.

"Uncle Ted has died," my brother said.

Last-minute checking of flights and comparing timing against a mountain trip on my motorcycle led to a 4 a.m. bitterly cold start from Edmonton, Alberta. The dark of the night a perfect setting for my experience of loss.

Three and a half hours later, shaking with cold, I pulled up to a rustic wooden building painted the dark brown of "I belong to the woods." Cline River, Alberta, my first stop. I'm here early, they are just now opening for breakfast.

Even the snowmobile-grade gloves, layers of wool under my motorcycle jacket, and multiple layers of wool socks have not kept me warm. I need fuel to stoke my body's furnace. Stiff with cold, my dismount from the bike is slow. I've been riding through the cold and dark for so long that my body complains—vigorously. I look up, the promise of a grey morning just hinted at by a not-quite-as-dark sky as I head inside.

Numb fingers slowly wrap around hot tea. Numb thoughts slowly wrap around the hollow space left by the call. Yes, the pain is still there, pushed back, suspended from my reality by the incomprehensible thought that my favourite uncle is gone. Not really my uncle, but my dad's lifelong best friend. At ages seven and eight, they ran away from the farm in Crooked Creek, Alberta, heading towards Edmonton— too many chores. They were going to get 'paying jobs'. My dad's oldest brother Edwin was sent to bring them back. My dad and Uncle Ted played together, went through puberty together, got into trouble together, worked together, and even wanted to date the same woman, my mother. Like everything else they ever disagreed about, they worked it out. Uncle Ted was always there at every holiday, at every excuse for a family gathering. Once, when he wasn't there, I said, "It's not Christmas without Uncle Ted!"—a sentiment shared by all.

Back on the road, the rising sun brought a welcome warmth. The brightness of the sun grasped at with a mind desperate to remember the good times, rather than this present loss. No longer as numb in mind or body, the memories come. As the kilometres pass, so does a parade of recollections. Running to be scooped up. A Christmas tree in the corner. The fascination of a half-lost finger probed at by a child.

A smile through my tears shocks me. How could I smile now? The paradox of intense grief linked with celebrating life is new to me. So I remember, I celebrate, and I grieve … and more memories come. A memory of my uncle is a memory of my dad. Inextricably linked by their closeness, my grief over my uncle touches the un-grieved places of my father's death.

The art of riding motorcycles requires a presence in the now that is as fluid as the mountain road I'm on. Subtle shifts in balance and light opposing pressure on the handlebars glide me around twists and turns. Being present includes all my emotions, this leads me inexorably deeper into the grief of losing my father. A gentle rain falls from a sky turned grey, drops gather and move with the wind across my visor. Inside the visor, tears gather and stream down my face, the rain a curious permission to finally cry. Not that I did not cry when my dad died. I did, but this time the tears are full and encompass life as well as death. I had been closed to the aliveness of walking fully through pain—too afraid of the pain itself. Closing the heart that hurts also closes it to joy, to beauty, to savouring the moments.

The nature of motorcycling around a winding road is one of sudden reveals: a tumultuous river, a serene lake, a stand of vibrant trees, the essence of a mountain. The enduring stone of the mountain speaks to my bones—I expand. Riding 'uncaged' leaves one close to this beauty, a song in the blood around each corner, a savouring of beauty. I move into the sensuality of flowing around the turns. All of this allows me to see the beauty around me, and the beauty and truth within my own story. A lively awareness of the closeness of death is once more linked to my own renewed aliveness. A part of my essential journey, life and death, each more vibrant together.

The mountain elevations and twists and turns have passed, as have delays for unexpected construction. The road now soft and easy beside Shuswap Lake lying calm and still, perfectly reflecting what is. Just as I now ride deep in peace, calm and stillness, accepting.

Late for a funeral I no longer need.

Azmina Kassam

The Final Hour

This piece is in honour of Arne Olsen, the man so loved and respected by so many, who by his actions opened hearts. He continues to influence my thoughts, my words, and my deeds. He passed away on September 05, 2012.

Vancouver, January 13, 2016, 10 p.m. on a Wednesday night. I feel like a pack rat in my lofty apartment off of sixth and Granville. Night has ascended quickly. The prevalent mood is one of nostalgia. Boccelli laments words about love from his album 'Amore'. Something about his voice, the intensity of his tone, the pleading nature of his words, raw with emotion, resonates with my own state of feelings. Memories of my beloved in the final hour of his life, play out in my mind like a scratched record.

⤺

Wednesday morning, September 05, 2012, 9 a.m., my gentle giant, once a debonair Viking, now lying in a tender heap of fragile bones and dry skin, bruised and blotchy with unhealed scarring from the intravenous needles that poked through his thin flesh. His body still warm, resting beside me, hands folded at his heart centre, like a precious baby. His spirit wanes between worlds. A box of pills, oxycodone, hydromorphine, and lyrica, some in liquid form and others in a pill form for pain relief. His life had narrowed dramatically to the point of keeping him as comfortable as possible. It was time for him to take his medicine. I reach over to touch his forehead, he felt warm as I kissed his cheek damp with moisture from the night.

"Arne, Sweetheart, what is going on, how are you my love?" I nudged him gently.

A pause, there was no answer. His mouth was slightly ajar. I pick up the phone, my heart racing,

"Renee, he is not answering, he is still breathing," my voice trails off.

Renee, the head nurse in charge of Arne's care has given me the permission to call her any time. She picks up the receiver. She hears my tone, "I'll be there as soon as I can, stay beside him, hold his hand, I will be there soon," she reassures me.

Renee, like the Doctor at VGH, had insinuated that Arne did not have long to live. I had been in denial so desperately wanting to keep him alive, feeding him homemade chicken stock three times a day, mushy rice with milk and sugar, congee. He made faces squishing up his nose in disgust but he would make an effort to drink the chicken stock. Anything to nourish him, feed him and keep him alive. He had become so thin. The doses of prednisone prescribed for his failing digestive system eroded the calcium from his bones, leaving his body distorted, in a crippled state and suffering the pain of multiple fractures. He could barely stand upright.

"Death is so final ... soon it will be my turn," he had said to me only days before.

The inevitability and finality of death brings on an echo of utter helplessness and hopelessness.

Sensing the increasing loss of his life force, I held his hand in the warmth of mine. The evening before, Arne had struggled to finish the small bowl of Cream of Wheat prepared the way he liked, with lots of milk, a dab of butter, sprinkled with brown sugar, and ground up cinnamon. His pride would not allow me or anyone else to feed him. Once fiercely independent and athletic, he had encouraged me to take tennis lessons. He made me a member of a tennis club and together we played countless doubles matches. He introduced me to downhill skiing, and on our first trip to Whistler together he took me up to seventh heaven and urged me to ski down to meet my instructor. He challenged my fears. He also indulged my passions and arranged walking trips through

Tuscany, France, and the Lake District in England. He encouraged me to swim naked in the cold water at Heron rocks and swam effortlessly with me across the bay outside his property on Hornby Island.

And now we both were witness to the tremendous effort it took to lift the teaspoon half heaped with cereal towards his mouth, his thin lips just barely parted. He motioned me towards the drawer beside the bed. I opened it and saw in it a velvet blue box. He prompted me to open it. Inside, lying soft against a white satin fabric was a luminous blue mother of pearl, oval-shaped pendant hanging from a sterling chain. A little note beside it read:

"I will love you even after I am gone."

I could only imagine the energy involved in having this gift ready for me to receive from him in his most delicate hour. He motioned for me to put it on. I did.

I asked him if he had seen a vision of his mother, Gina, who had instilled in him a rich tradition of Christian values. I had experienced this in the way he lived his life, where money was never made to be an issue even when he did not have much, he constantly gave it away. He rarely said no. The sign of seeing his mother in the form of an apparition, a dream or a voice represented for me a sign that the end was near. He nodded ever so slowly as if to say 'yes'. His hand continued to quiver in the warmth of mine. Unable to hold back the tears, I let go of his hand and sought refuge in the dark and private space of our bathroom. The pastel tones and textures of cream and stone, the dimmed lights and the running of water from the open tap helped me to hide the sounds of my sobbing. The time with him was precious. I had to be the strong one now to carry us both through this final farewell. He gazed at me, his eyes filled with adoration as I reached for his hand. I had become his lifeline, where before he had been mine. Love is a strange and mysterious thing. Our worlds collided bringing us together, despite our large age difference of twenty-nine years apart. I was thirty-three and never been married and he was fifty-eight and on his third divorce. We were from different cultural and religious persuasions, he was Christian and I was a practicing Ismaili, Muslim. My family, particularly my father felt betrayed by my decision to move in with Arne. I had decided against marrying a man deemed 'suitable' by the family and it took some time before my father was ready to forgive me and speak to me again.

Arne was starting to slip away and there was nothing in the world that I could do to hold him back, but surrender to the mystery, the void into whose vastness I knew we must all disperse into like vapor someday. This was the primal juncture where death would intercede life and the reality of a permanent separation looms.

Nine a.m. on a Wednesday morning, his hands are cool to touch, his eyes are closed and the sound of his breath is on pause. By the time Renee arrives, there is nothing left of his spirit, and the body has become a hollowed vessel, cold and stark. Seventy-six years of an entire life dissolved in a single out breath.

Three years later I have moved into a small loft-style apartment framed in high ceilings, with large pieces of art adorning the walls. Bocelli's 'amore' reverberates through the large eight feet by three foot panels painted in a Leonardo da Vinci style of pointillism depicting angels with wings, blowing trumpets, their faces turned upwards, with flowing garments in shades of soft greys and ivory, stepping up to heaven. Comforted by the beauty and relevance of Sam Lam's 'The Angels' which had lived with Arne and I in our bedroom at Pennyfarthing, close to Granville Island and which I now woke up to every morning in the sacred space of my loft.

I recalled with nostalgia the magnitude of my past knowing there was a finite quality to all things. I often thought of the words I spoke at Arne's eulogy:

"When we are stripped of everything, the only things that remain are the memories of the time we spent together and the love that we shared."

Perhaps the time had come to surrender the Angels and to allow for a renaissance of other experiences to emerge where the realm of possibilities could be infinite. Perhaps the time had come to really say "Farewell my love, I have loved you well and you my Love have been the wings that have set me free."

Before Arne passed he asked me to have the words from the Book of John engraved on his plaque to read:

And Jesus said:
Love one another as I have Loved you

Arne lived these words till his last breath.

Eric Macnaughton
The Box

At the time my grandfather died, my family's story was stuck in the present, mired in unhappy circumstance: my parent's divorce, my brother's hospitalization, my own uncertain future. When my grandmother handed my grandfather's personal effects to me, there was an opening: one I curiously ventured through, seeking rootedness, perhaps some Arcadian past.

My grandfather's archives were scant. For the most part, the contents fit inside a small metal box, dusty rose with intricate gold overlay, which once held Moirs chocolates. I imagined the box to have been a gift from my grandfather to his first wife, Florence, the birth grandmother I'd never known. I imagined Florence using it for her keepsakes. I imagined my grandfather adding his own after she died. I opened up the box and looked inside.

I read a fraying newspaper clipping about my great uncle Don—he'd won the Maritimes golf championship; a yellowed telegram conveying his triumph to my grandfather, addressed to the Saranac Lake Sanitorium in upstate New York, where he was recovering from tuberculosis.

I studied a picture of him and Florence on their wedding day, posed on the edge of Trinity Bay, Newfoundland; and a photo of my three-year old dad, in helmet and sailor suit, next to his unsmiling, wizened grandfather, out front of the family cottage at Cape Brulé, New Brunswick, not too far from their home in Moncton.

I also examined a later photo of my dad, age twelve, with his new best friend ("Irish Protestant!"[phew!] Florence had written on the back)— opening presents on the first Christmas at 68 Church Street, their new home in Kitchener, Ontario; and flipped through a small yellow photo album belonging to Florence, of Maritimes people and events that meant nothing to me, and which my dad had long forgotten after he'd moved away, and his mom's death shortly after.

The last photograph I looked at, taken many years later, was of my twin brother and me around the same age as my sailor-suited father, on the beach at Cape Brulé. It is an idyllic looking spot, but one that I can't remember ever having been. I understand the place was sold not too long after our visit, no longer a convenient gathering place for the far-flung family.

I picked up my grandfather's family tree, the Parkins of New Brunswick, bound up in soft cover as a small blue pocketbook, compact enough to fit inside the box. On an inside page were daguerreotype reproductions, ancient likenesses of my great, great, great, great grandparents, John and Elizabeth Parkin, who had carved a farm out of the wilderness on the Coverdale River, near present-day Moncton. The chapters articulated the lineage of each of their thirteen offspring.

I focused closely on the second one, about Ann, my direct ancestor, born in 1823, the oldest daughter amongst thirteen siblings. I followed it down through the generations. I stopped at a great great uncle, "Benjamin Franklin Macnaughton, MD". I reached the entry about my dad ("Bill has a Ph.D. in American Literature" it read), and the one about my brother and me ("Paul and Eric are identical twins" was our claim to immortality; my sister had yet to be born, when the book was compiled.)

I absorbed some arresting material in the other chapters (a sister with mental illness who died in a farmhouse fire, a deathbed confession of an illegitimate child, the family legend of its matriarchs' origin, as the offspring of a "wandering member of the House of Hanover.") I came to the last chapter.

Here, I read about George, the thirteenth and youngest, and the only sibling to get any sort of education. For someone born in the back-woods of New Brunswick in 1846, the entry outlined an unbelievable trajectory: attending Normal School to become a teacher, graduating from University of New Brunswick (magna cum laude), securing appointments as Headmaster of Fredericton Collegiate (the province's highest teaching appointment), then as Headmaster of Upper Canada College, and finally as Founding Secretary of the Rhodes Scholarship; following that, receiving honorary doctorates from Oxford, Padua, and finally, knighthood.

Though the name George Parkin meant nothing to me, I noted others down his line that did, branching off, and connecting through marriage. There was son-in-law Vincent Massey, the first Canadian-born Governor General. There was Omar Pound, Ezra Pound's son, and Parkin's grandson-in- law. And then, more "George's": grandson George Grant (I'd just finished reading his Lament for a Nation); and grandson-in-law George Ignatieff.

Not too long before, as University of Toronto Chancellor, he'd conferred my undergraduate degree upon me. I remember the stultifying ceremony, shuffling like cattle, waiting to go up on stage.

But I also remember approaching him, seeing his genuine smile, the twinkle in his eyes, gazing directly into mine, hearing him say in a deep rich voice: "Congratulations, Mister Macnaughton!" I felt that he knew me.

Reading through all the names and story fragments, I thought about how strange it was that my grandfather had never mentioned any of this, and that my dad was unaware of these connections. Along with this feeling of strangeness, I also felt some sense of coherence: the familial mental illness, the bookishness.

I wondered if it helped explain my brother's hospitalization. I wondered if it helped explain how my dad, who had grown up in a house with few books, became a man of letters. I pondered my own graduation ceremony. I wondered about how young George, the thirteenth sibling, had made it out of the bush, to become "Dr. Parkin", and then "Sir George", an Honourary Knight of the Round Table.

I put the small blue book back in its box. I closed the lid. I sealed the memories away. I wondered about the story behind it all. I went back to my life.

Natasha Barber

Meanderings
of a
Bizarre Year

I am curled up on the couch in the living room with my feet tucked under me and my notebook on my lap. There is something about writing in this way that enables me to be vulnerable and truly put what is in my heart and mind on the page. It would allow anyone who read my journals to have an understanding of my life experiences and how they impacted me from how I think and feel about myself to my understanding of my place in the world. As such, these pages are sacred and never to be shared.

The patio door is open and outside the sun pushes through the pine tree towering above the house to create a mottled pattern on the deck. For a brief moment, I transition to sitting outside until the pulsing heat from the sun prompts me to return to the cool shadows of the interior of the house. Regardless of whether or not I am inside or outside, I can hear birds chirp and the rolling throng of the engines of planes soaring overhead. The planes come and go at random, circling high above, keeping watch on us below.

It is Monday. A day I should be at work, but earlier this year I had a breakdown, or as a wise woman suggested, "a breakthrough". For me, this latter title offers a better understanding since that is exactly what transpired—forgotten memories broke through.

Interestingly, this moment did not happen like a flip of the switch or the snap of the fingers. Instead, it transpired over a period of months—

terrifying and exhausting months. The instigating factor of the break-through matters little. What I will share is that somehow my infertility struggles collided with the awareness of my father's passing like two freight trains going in opposite directions. The cargo, my memories, splattered all around waiting for me to save some from fires, piece to-gether broken bits, and line other parts up in sequenced rows.

The collision happened fast and quick, but the inner turmoil asso-ciated with the crash lingered and if it was not for medication to help sop up residual buzzing anxiety and energy sapping depression, I still might simply be pacing about the wreckage wondering what I should do. Instead, I am still surveying the wreckage of my life and finally my eyes have been opened to truths I was unable to see before. Such is the nature of trauma.

Slowly over the past half a year the blinders I had constructed, i.e., ways of filtering my life to enable me to keep going, began to retract and memories I had forgotten began to take shape. I have begun to look through the wreckage and work to piece together what lay outside of my consciousness for so long. This awakening is a story in itself and I will save that for another day because I could not do it justice now since I am still not fully aware of the "process" of removing my blinders.

The bodily sensations that accompanied this awakening can be lik-ened to a constant stream of electricity cruising through my body and brain. Unlike Frankenstein in Mary Shelley's book (the constructed man who got one zing of electricity thanks to lightning—not minimiz-ing being hit by lightning at all, just trying to find a decent comparison), I felt I was charged 24-7 with electricity, with the intensity at night being the worst. I would lay there as my lungs and rib cage vibrated so strongly I felt they would surge out of my body. What this must have looked like to my husband who lay beside me I can only assume would look like mo-ments in movies where someone passes away on an operating table and they get the Code Blue cart, the one with the paddles to shock the heart so it functions again. In these scenes, accurate or not—I have no idea—the chest rises with the charge surging through the chest while the arms and legs tense. I think that must have been my relaxed sleeping position (hope you see the sarcasm) for about three months, my trying to lie still and contain the energy surging through my body. At first, I was not able to make sense of whatever was screaming for my attention (you know how what you really need to pay attention to takes the form of night-mares ... well my subconscious not only increased my awareness in the form of nightmares, it also jostled me when I was awake and aware). I be-gan to have moments where what I needed to pay attention to smacked me alert. I was wading through the wreckage of the train collision and starting to actually see what constituted the debris.

I became helpless as memories arose like stars in the night sky. The notion that where someone lives impacts what stars they can see (i.e., they can remember). If someone lives in the city (or close to things that evoke painful memories), they will not see as much as someone who lives in the country (far away from triggers for painful memories). So, simi-larly where someone lives will impact what they can remember. Some-times it is safest to lie to oneself. It is a form of survival. That said, there is the notion that more stars will be seen in the country, but sometimes people know more stars exist, yet they are not ready or not able to choose to go and verify that the stars actually rest in the sky. So they choose to stay in the city and only look at what is safe to see.

Moving on with the stars analogy, as more and more memories arose and I was able to see more and more stars, I began to notice patterns, or constellations, as the memories began to cluster together. At this mo-ment, things still feel so distant like the stars and again for the purpose of this essay this is as far as I will go with this topic.

Interestingly, during this period of time I reconnected with a part of me I had forgotten. It took the form of an angst-driven teen who, regard-less of wisdom, acted out in deliberate opposition to what was in our best interest. I was remembering things that evoked strong emotions of suffering such as devastation, hurt, and pain that I wanted to fight back.

I never was allowed to fight back as a teen. I had to take the burden of my father's warped mind and hold all of his evil within me in order to keep other people safe. So, at this point in my life where the worst and most evil monster you could imagine had passed away—booyah—my freeze (of the fight, flight, and freeze survival mode) popped into fight mode. Yay inner teen!

In my present day life, these acts took the form of self-sabotage. It was too challenging to go to that vulnerable place when everything in my life felt so unpredictable and my husband struggled to look me in the eye. It was best to circle like an eagle. At some point, I will be able to land (though I dream of swooping down to grab my prey, those who have chosen to technologically abuse me), but until then, I still feel exposed and vulnerable as a result of my memories and the associated emotions, fear and shame. As such, it is best to keep some memories to myself until I find the words to share them.

I have looked evil in the eye and survived once before and I can and will do it again. I am stronger than the memories that haunt me. My body wants to heal so I know without a doubt I will be fine but, until I am able to see the full wreckage and recount the debris I will remain cryptic, finding refuge in the shadows of poetic lingo. A notion that pairs with a Jungian concept in which the idea of trying to put words to a story too soon will lead to the death and loss of that story. I do not wish to thrust my story out into the glaring light of consciousness before it is ready. If I did, it would be much like taking a mythical creature who lives in the shadows of the forest and forcing that creature into the field into the sunlight. If this is done, the mythical creature will turn to stone and all life is lost. I wish to retain and keep all of my memories, even those from terrifying moments when I kicked into survival mode. Everything I have been through has shaped me and helped me become the person I am today. Everything has purpose and meaning in my life, even the difficult stuff.

Carolyn Bentley

Magic Hour

AN EXCERPT

Two hundred crew gather in a clearing on the set where the Arikara warriors will attack the fur trapper's camp. I shuffle and move with the group to form a huge circle on the edge of the Bow River. The morning sun takes off the chill and the Rockies cup the horizon in the deep background. The circle widens to accommodate the last few cast members and stunt men on horseback. Hand holds hand, touches horse, and then human hand again. The circle settles and is complete.

Our director steps forward.

"I woke up this morning and I could not believe this day has finally arrived. I have been thinking about this moment for three years. This is the realization of a dream. We are embarking on a great journey together as a family, older crew with great experience and newer ones, bringing in fresh energy."

An Elder lights a sage stick and smudges the director, fans the smoke around his body with eagle feathers tied together to form a wing three feet long. His movements are slow and deliberate as he works his way around the circle, offering the smudge to each person. The circle is big. I realize this is going to take time. I look to the Assistant Directors, the time keepers of the set, and try to detect agitation but see none. I settle into the silence. Three Elders, bundled in 1970s style down jackets, legs wrapped in navy plaid blankets, sit in flimsy folding lawn chairs, singing and chanting. Our director continues to speak.

"I want to thank our hosts for generously allowing us to be here on their land. This movie, for me, is about spiritual enlightenment through physical pain. I want to tell this story as honestly as possible. I thank you all for coming on this journey with me. The Elders are here to sing us in, to ask for protection, and the assistance of the ancestors as we make this journey together.

I make my way across the trapper camp set, bridging worlds between the present and the nineteenth century American frontier world of the fur traders and the ancestral lands they traversed.

I pass work areas dressed with axes, knives, tools and bloody rags, campfires rigged with hidden propane lines for flames, bales of fake beaver pelts tied together with thick twine, a wooden hut. Puddles form between downed logs in the uneven ground. A minimal stand of tall pine trees rooted in the packed solid mud ground sway in the wind. Anchors are hammered into their trunks to attach the cables for stunt work. Tree branches that will be set on fire are rigged and attached to their rough bark. A replica flatboat floats in the river, anchored in place.

I head up the hill to the circus that is arranged on the plateau above. It's a collection of converted semi-trailers, 5-tons, 10-tons, RVs, and special event tents all adapted one way or another to accommodate film-making. I think of it as an old western movie where the settlers circle the wagons, only these wagons are trailers and we are not under attack.

The extras and stunt tents buzz with activity. The uneven plywood floors buckle with the hustle of forty stunt warriors, thirty-five stunt trappers, and fifty background performers going through hair, make-up, and wardrobe.

A warrior pulls a simple leather tunic over his head, flicks his long dark hair over his back and puts on a bear tooth necklace. He ties his leather leggings to a loincloth with leather straps, then securely ties up his moccasins.

The trapper next to him, in brown wool pants, tucks in a faded pin-stripe collarless shirt and stretches the button-on suspenders over each shoulder, right then left, buttons up his chevron weave vest and knots a scarf around his neck. He stamps his feet a couple of times on the plywood floor, testing out his worn leather ankle boots.

A couple of warriors dressed in costume stand by a rusty red coloured metal shipping container, eating foil-wrapped breakfast burritos. A gust of wind picks up the heavy steel door and slams it shut.

"Must be the ancestors," I catch one say.

"I hope they're not pissed," says the other.

I stop and feel the air around me. Send out psychic antennae, press against the atmosphere and ask:

"Are you angry?"

"No. We are here. We are all around you. We are not angry."

"I didn't think so. Just checking."

I walk across the plateau, past the corral where the picture horses are being held. A make-up artist brushes war paint on a horse—a thick white circle around its eye, a big brown beautiful eye with lashes to die for, patiently looking back at her. The ochre stripes on his rib cage are drying.

I look into the eye and wonder what mystery it holds. What secrets, what answers? I wish I could reach inside this horse and magically pull out a speaking soul that will reveal the secrets of the world and ease all my fears. I know you're hiding in there. I know you know. I see you.

The dog wranglers throw balls for their dogs from the back of open hatchbacks.

A stray German shepherd cross pup with a sun-bleached tattered bandana around its neck wanders in from the Reserve, eats out of any hand that appears with a bit of donut or bacon, flops down in the dry grass, bloated tummy exposed and growing before my eyes.

We have been rehearsing this sequence for weeks and today is the first day of filming. It's a complex dance, a brutal massacre choreographed to recreate the horror of a surprise attack.

We are using only natural light, no artificial lighting, so the special window of time needed to capture the attack on camera is the short window of time before sunset, the "magic hour", when all the action will be captured by the ARRI Alexa camera, designed to suck up every piece of natural light.

Finally, it's time to shoot. I stand beside an arid pine tree, hold on and watch. As the sun goes down, all hell breaks loose.

Warriors on horseback gallop along the ridge and accelerate down the embankment into camp. Arrows fly, gunfire explodes. The wounded fall off horses and splash face down into puddles. Legs are blown off. Cries and commands pepper the air. Dogs bolt and scatter, run wildly away. The wounded claw and crawl, looking for cover. A tall nude trapper with his pants down around his ankles and an arrow in his back is dragged on his stomach into the false safety of camp. It is complete and total mayhem. Fires burn, smoke fills the air, tents catch on fire, tree branches erupt into flames. Riderless horses rear and dodge in random directions, their powerful flanks flexing in slow motion, hooves skating over the muddy terrain searching for traction. A defenseless amputee lies propped up against a tree. Blood surges from his vacant limb. A trapper breaks free and sprints into the clearing, heading to the hut for cover. He is hit with three arrows; one to his back and two others pierce each hamstring. He's down, face first in a horse piss puddle. His brother screams "Billy", sprints after him, falters and falls dead. Another trapper, with a massive stomach wound, staggers holding his gut as blood and intestines ooze out between his fingers. He makes it to the shack and collapses.

"Cut! Cut! Blood, blood. More blood. We need more blood."

The director runs over to the key make-up artist, shouting.

"This is a massacre you idiot. Look at this guy. His guts are falling out of his stomach. This isn't a little Disneyland scratch. He's holding his guts in his hands. We need more blood. Think about it. You should be ashamed."

The make-up artist freezes and pales.

The director grabs the bottle of blood out of his hand, unscrews the lid and sloshes the entire contents over the trapper lying play-dead on the ground.

The smells of mud and shit and horse piss fill my senses. The taste of charcoal smoke that no amount of water can wash away coats my mouth, the collision of screaming voices on the radio vying for airtime fills my head through the tiny radio earpiece wedged inside my right ear lobe. This is like being at war.

Lakshmi Iyer

Life Lessons

Dear Ammu, Pattu and Laddu,

Over the years I have written many little notes to you. Some were on Post-its that found their way to trash the next day. Some have been on my blog which talk about you at a specific age. Some are birthday wishes. Some are celebrations of milestones. Today, however, I am writing because of some morbid thoughts in my head.

I am forty. I am at the age where I see some of my friends die way too soon. I see people like me leave behind families and spouses and it hits me that someday it could be me. That it could be us.

I have dreams for you, for us. I envision you and I becoming good friends someday, but before that I will need to be a parent to you. I want to see you go to college, spread your wings and fly. I want to see you married and mother children of your own.

Sometimes, I worry I may not have that chance. In no particular order, I want to share with you the things I have learned. In the event I am not around, I hope you will sense my presence as you read this.

⌒

TELL THE TRUTH

It is simple. Tell the truth all the time. It will not be easy but it will save you from heartache. Whether it is owning up to messing up your life or pretending to be busy so you can avoid something you committed to, choose truth over lies. Uncomfortable definitely, but worth the peace of mind.

SAY SORRY AND MEAN IT

We all mess up. Saying sorry when you are in the wrong offers a way forward. Own up to your mistake and put it out in the open. Apologize and mean it. You will be amazed how many conflict-ridden situations can be smoothed over by a heartfelt sorry.

SPEAK YOUR MIND

If your friend asks you for a favour and you would rather not spend your time on it, speak up and say what you think. Much like telling the truth, speaking up for how you feel is important. It is uncomfortable. It risks the relationship. It also makes the relationship stronger. It frees you up to be the person you are rather than the person someone else wants you to be.

KEEP YOUR PROMISES

This has been my toughest challenge. I often over-promise and under-deliver and feel wretched about it. If you promise to do something, do it. Integrity is hard won and something that will be recognized life-long.

WALK THE WALK

As your mom, I have often noticed you do not do what I say. You do as I act. Words are less powerful than actions. Model the behaviours you want someone else to emulate. Before you advise someone to quit smoking or stop drinking make sure you model those behaviours yourself.

FALL IN LOVE

Yes, you heard me right. Fall in love, get your heart broken. Feel with all your being. Few things in life are worth risking everything for, and love is one of them. You will be heartbroken. You will mope and cry. You will pick up and move on. But guess what, you will have experienced one of the best things in life. Love makes you vulnerable. It makes you put someone else ahead of you. It makes you see beauty everywhere. It is truly a joyous thing.

SPEND LESS THAN YOU EARN

Common sense, right? You will be surprised how simple things are the hardest to follow. Earn an honest living. Spend within your means. Save what you can. Do not borrow. These are small edicts that will keep you solvent and happy. Money cannot buy happiness but it can keep you comfortable.

DONATE

Set aside a small percentage of what you earn to share with the less privileged. It does two things. It reminds you of all that is well in your life. It opens your eyes to the needs of others. The amount does not matter. Pick something you are comfortable with but do it year over year. All life long.

LOVE MEANS RESPECT

As you grow, you will discover boys (or girls). You will discover the joys of romantic love. Your world will shrink to the two of you. It is easy to be taken in, easy to give up your identity to take on another. I want you to know and remember that love also means respect. A partner who does not recognize you as an individual and does not respect you, has no place in your life. Retain a strong sense of self, even when in love. Especially when in love.

FOLLOW YOUR HEART, BUT USE YOUR BRAIN

There will come a time when you are in high school and the question of what to do with your life will come up. When I was in high school, I knew in my heart that writing was my calling. However, I followed my peers and signed up for Math and Physics. I became a software engineer. I do not regret my choice but that is only because I was able to earn my way to financial independence. Now, I write, which is what I love to do. When you are faced with the decision, look at all the options and pick something that will let you earn your way to doing what you love to do. Sometimes, it may happen that what you love is also something that will make a successful professional out of you. If that happens, count yourself lucky.

DISCOVER YOURSELF
Find the things that make you happy. Pick a hobby. Set time aside to do the things you love to do. Create an identity for yourself that will set you apart from your family. Nurture it. Do it when times are good. Do it when times are rough. Create an oasis to which you can retreat when the world outside is overwhelming.

MAKE FRIENDS, BUT LEARN TO LET GO
The only constant in life is change. Learn to nurture meaningful friendships. Treasure these relationships with your life. Relationships need work but they also need both parties to make the effort. If you find yourself giving more than you get, re-evaluate and move on.

YOUR LIFE, YOUR WAY
Much too often, you will have others tell you how you should live, how you should look, what you should do and what is good for you. It is great that you have so many people looking out for you, but the key is knowing what you want. Always remember, it is your life. What you want from it comes first. Listen to your inner voice and follow your gut. The people in your life? They will come around.

LOVE YOURSELF
It is true. It took me forty years to realize that self-love is the best love. It has taken me all of my life to look in the mirror and love me the way I am. Skinny or fat, fair or dark, the world we live in has impossible standards for beauty and acceptance. Love yourself the way you are. Dress

for comfort. Own yourself and rock it. Always remember that it is what is inside that counts.

Always remember Appa and I are here for you. So long as one of us are alive, we have your back. Remember, we are just one call away.

Love, Amma.

Lucía I. Terra

The Best Line of Defence

AN EXCERPT

Totalitarian regimes fear stories. Whenever dictators seize power, their first move is to suppress people's voices. They burn books, close libraries, persecute and torture intellectuals, silence storytellers. Even with all their tanks and guns, what they fear most is paper and pen.

As a military regime took over my country the year I was born, the world outside was quickly shut down and a blanket of silence covered us. Their version of the world—hierarchical, oppressive, violent—pervaded everything. Books became my only escape. I was almost obsessively drawn to them: they took me to places I couldn't go, introduced me to people I couldn't meet, showed that other realities existed. Untouched by the World Outside, I lived for and through books.

The quest to decode the secrets in those pages started early. I couldn't wait for Mom to have time to read them to me—there was so much waiting to be read. So, I taught myself to read. I showed up in the kitchen carrying a heavy book over my head, opened on a certain page, my little index finger as bookmark. I juggled the book in front of Mom and asked her which letter was this or that one. I made my way back to the living room, repeating the sound to myself, eyes fixed on the new letter. That way, I kept on with the slow work of deciphering the secret codes. I strung words together and letter by letter added them to construct the sentences that allowed me to find out—finally—what was hidden in that particular page. A whole page later, while the meat roasted beside the potatoes and the tomato sauce simmered to perfection, Mom wiped her hands on her apron and took a moment to sit by my side on the green vinyl couch to relieve me from my strenuous work, for another page, perhaps two.

That hard labour would go on for days and days, as I preferred the hefty volumes in our library. My thing was the nature encyclopaedias flaunting far away lands and exotic animals. Mine, too, was the grown-up versions of children's classics—the full-length tales originally meant for adults that were later cut into simpler versions for small people. My Gulliver didn't just travel to the country of the Lilliput and the giants; he visited many other strange places, including the cloud-country of algebraic crazies and the fascinating world where horses ruled and spoke their own language. *My* Peter Pan didn't just take Wendy into Neverland; I knew him as Peter the small child first and found out how he became Pan. And so too with the travels of Nils over the Nordic fjords on the back of a goose, the adventures of the children of Captain Grant on the southern plains of Patagonia, and the several volumes of Sandokan, the Tiger of Malaysia, sailing along the coast of Borneo. I didn't discriminate when it came to reading: anything in print that crossed my path would do. I read right and left, kids, youth, and adult's literature, in my language or foreign ones, fiction, reference books, and dictionaries alike. This was in part because there was not much to choose from. Books were expensive, and public libraries had been strangled under the military regime until they became dusty, dying archives. As I ran out of new things to read at home, I raided any bookcase I could access. Every time we visited family or friends, after the mandatory rounds of greetings, I snuck to the room with books.

In Grandma's house the situation was tricky. The bookcase was in the living room, where everybody gathered. But I had a strategy figured out. I hurried to sit on the sofa across from the books and pulled my young brother to my left side, a human shield that kept me out of my stern grandma's field of vision. Meanwhile, my parents, uncles, and aunts sat to my right. Under that arrangement, while the conversation criss-crossed over my head, I was safe to study the covers of the books and magazines in front of me, looking for the next target. My eyes darted to the line of thin yellow covers on the bottom shelf—a centipede of *National Geographic* magazines, hopefully with a new issue among them. After an hour or so of catching up with news and family gossip, things loosened up. People moved around, stood to serve some sweets, went to the bathroom. Now was the time: I pointed towards the bottom shelf of the library and whispered to Mom, "Can I read one?" Without skipping a beat, Mom nodded. I scanned the yellow line one more time, picked the newest issue, sat back in my place, and disappeared into strange lands.

I didn't understand a word of English at that time, but that wasn't a barrier. I was drawn to the magnificent pictures of impossible geographies, the wild-looking animals, the striking faces of people. The kaleidoscope of humans in the photos amazed me. We, for the most part, were brownish. We saw the world through hazel eyes, our faces were framed by chestnut hair, and shades of pale beige went through the skin of my family. In contrast, the people on the pages were sometimes translucent white with bright yellow hair and very, very pale blue eyes. Or they were black, black, so black as blue, so black that I had to squint to distinguish the features in the photo. They wore elaborate dresses with fancy patterns—nothing like the dullness of our simple blues, greys, and browns, our plain jeans *vaqueros* and sport shoes *championes*, our cotton т-shirts and wool pullovers. The pages of the magazine exploded also with polychrome houses, an unimaginable contrast to the sombre bricks and grey cement of our city.

I was told to leaf through with extreme caution, careful not to leave marks and not to cut my fingers on the thick shiny paper. The sacred status of those foreign magazines couldn't be explained by the pleasure of reading. Grandma, who grew up in the countryside at the beginning of the century, didn't read English. As for Grandpa … French was still the foreign language of choice for their generation. None of their children had more than a rudimentary grasp of the language either, probably insufficient for the rich expressions favoured by *National Geographic* writers. Yet, maybe because of their sleek appearance and shiny pages, maybe because of their connection to the outer world and its promising freedom, the magazines were worshipped in my family. Those at Grandma's house all seemed to be brand new. We were supposed to keep them like that: no sign of leafing through them, no bent corners, no fingerprints, nor, god forbid, food stains. Even when my parents got a subscription of their own, the magazines maintained their high status as something precious to take care of and preserve. Yet, that was not true for everyone.

One afternoon, I worked on an assignment at a classmate's house. He and his family were expats, and as such, on the affluent side of things. They had lived abroad, which conferred on them a bit of an aura; they had been "outside." We were making a poster on Shanghai and needed images to spruce it up. My friend pulled a stack of *National Geographic* magazines, and we searched through them until we found a feature on Shanghai. I assumed we would make a photocopy and paint it. My friend, instead, picked up a pair of scissors and cut his way through the article leaving butchered pages and dangling strips of paper behind. I almost had a heart attack. "Are you sure?" I managed to stutter. Not a blink from my friend. He was already studying the best position to place the photos on our poster. Not until his mother showed up, gave a glance to our work and the chopped remains of the magazine, and congratulated us on the results, did I breathe. The striking photos, paired with a successful rendering of the Chinese characters for Shanghai, got us the best grade in the class. In my eyes, though, not even that justified the mutilation.

To this day, if you snoop around my library, you won't find a single book or magazine with a bent corner, not even a pencil mark. After all, books are still the best line of defence against tyrannical regimes.

Jennifer Simon

The Runaway

Wildflowers bloom mysteriously in untamed places, gently swaying in the warm breeze, inspiring a sense of freedom and random potency that's enviable.

In contrast, my well-ordered life had all the check marks on the metaphorical list, you know, the one good girls keep. A rewarding job as a French teacher in an affluent neighbourhood in Connecticut, a custom built home surrounded by orchards and equestrian trails, wonderful friends, a successful husband, and dream vacations; a compilation of everything I had strived for all those years. Fatefully brewing were the signs that I had followed the wrong map. Years of excuses about why the timing wasn't right for children, solo adventures, and a career that overshadowed our life. Thirteen years in, I finally heard the words that sounded too cliché to possibly be true.

"There is someone else."

I cried out with rage, surprised myself by throwing a nearby lamp against the wall. Then I heard an assured call from within, "Let go." So, I grabbed my keys and drove off in my Ford suv.

Given the state I was in, Lise and Kate were the only two people I wanted to connect with. We had been best friends since kindergarten and twenty-eight years later, we were still like sisters. I parked my car in a park near the Connecticut shoreline and called Lise to unload the story of my failed marriage. As I sobbed, she said, "You'll come here. You can stay with us. It will be okay. You'll see. But first we need a long weekend, just us girls."

It took six months to get everything squared away. I wrapped up the school year with a long planned trip to Quebec with my grade eight students, listed the house, worked out like a fiend, and drudged through the muck with a counsellor to figure out how I ended up in such a life of fiction. When the time was up, I signed a separation agreement, quit my job, packed my bags with only essentials, and left the furniture and boxes for the movers to take to storage, since I no longer had a home. I was heading back to British Columbia, with nothing but a broken me.

My flight landed in Victoria. After a weekend at my parent's farm, my Dad took me over on the ferry to Vancouver where we spent the day being tourists in a city that had been home only four years ago. Later, he dropped me off at Tim Horton's in North Vancouver to meet Kate.

Dad grabbed my gear out of the truck and walked me over to hug Kate. "It's been awhile. You look good, Kate." Her highlights and shoulder length hair framed her green eyes and her skin had a healthy glow paired with her lean and fit tall frame. As Kate opened the trunk of her silver Honda civic, my Dad placed the bags in the trunk causing the clank of the bottles. "So, it's gonna be one of *those* kind of runaways?" he chuckled. I looked at Kate recalling a time in high school when we tried to sneak out homemade wine by hiding it in a pop bottle and my Dad caught on to us. Her smile told me she remembered too.

"Thanks for the lift, Dad."

"Ah huh. Go have some fun. We'll see ya when we see ya."

As I slid in the front passenger side of the car, Kate handed me her iPod and said, "It's time for a trip down memory lane."

When I made out the heavy beat of the drums and the strong bass vocals of the Swiss band Yello repeating the simple and powerful lyrics, "Oh Yeah ..." my mind drifted to being thirteen again, when *Ferris Bueller's Day Off* had just hit theatres. I saw the movie five times. Maybe it was the cool, easy on the eyes, smooth-talking Ferris and his mantra, "Life moves pretty fast. If you don't stop and look around once in a while, you could miss it." It felt like a million moons ago.

The car stopped and jolted me back to reality. Lise bounced down the driveway and into the car. Her new pixie cut aged her, but she still bubbled like champagne that had just been uncorked, "Woo hoo! Four days of freedom!"

With the music of Toto singing "Africa" at full volume, we set off for Cortes Island. We had three ferries ahead of us, years of stories to catch up on, and the music of Michael Jackson, AC/DC, Indigo Girls, George Michael, Tom Petty, Lenny Kravitz, Journey, and The Red Hot Chili Peppers to fuel the journey.

It was ten-thirty in the evening by the time we arrived. Lise showed us around her family's cute little two bedroom cottage with a wrap-around front porch and peek-a-boo view of the ocean. I found my bed and crashed.

The next morning, we walked along a path lined with fields of wild-flowers to the Co-op Café for a latté and pain au chocolat. When we noticed the Free Store, Kate and Lise embarked on a mission to build me a new wardrobe. Their selections were everything except conservative. La pièce de résistance being a sequined fitted tank top in a midnight blue. "It's you, Jenn! It will make your eyes sparkle." Lise's compelling voice sold it like she was working on commission.

Later, we made our way to Hollyhock, an oceanfront retreat centre. We strolled through the flower garden, took photos and toured the gift shop before heading out to the veranda for lunch. I sat down in the chair closest to the deck railing and was stunned to see the long sandy beach lined with yoga mats and about twenty naked bodies performing child's pose. When they shifted to downward dog, we laughed uncontrollably. The hostess gave us a scolding look as we tried to regain our composure.

We returned to the cottage for a relaxing afternoon, followed by a Mexican fiesta, with freshly made guacamole, salsa and burritos. We added strawberry margaritas and danced to our favourite music. We reminisced about a boy nicknamed Mallow, short for marshmallow because he had no backbone, who spread a nasty rumour about Kate. We'd shown him. We took advantage of our next encounter at a local night-club by luring him outside behind a dumpster and stripping him, then running off before we got into any real trouble as Lise screamed at us, "Get in the car! The police are coming." Lise was always the one looking out for us, especially when we were our own worst enemies. As we recounted story after story, my eyes welled up with tears and laughter all at once. How had I forgotten how wild and free I once was?

We accepted an invite to a community party where we were greeted by friendly locals who offered us punch spiked with who knows what. People surrounded a bonfire, kids played with beach balls, others danced, many chatted away, and a few made figure eights with balls of fire, known as poi. The trees were covered with coloured lanterns and Christmas lights were streamed across the stage. There was a band playing reggae music and I recognized Bob Marley's "Stir It Up" right away. The punch went down easily and the atmosphere was electric.

Kate found her element self-dancing in the grassy field.

"What brings you to Cortes?"

I looked behind me to see who the tall smooth skinned guy was talking to, stunned by how striking he was with his with jet black hair and piercing pale blue eyes.

Lise jumped in, "We're on a girls' runaway weekend."

"What are you running from?" He smirked.

I interrupted with, "It's a long story."

He looked at me intently, "Would you like to dance?"

I shook my head, "That's nice of you ..." I felt Kate shove me from behind.

"Come on." Then he grabbed my hand.

The band sang, "We're here for a good time not a long time ..." A Trooper song I remembered well from high school. More Bob Marley followed. Then The Steve Miller Band, "Some people call me the space cowboy, some call me the doctor of love ... I'm a joker ..." We kept dancing as he bent down to ask my name.

"Jenn." I answered.

He responded with, "I'm Matt."

Then, I recognized the first few notes of my favourite song and I let out a squeal, "She's a good girl, loves her momma, loves Jesus and America too …"

Instantly, my body knew what to do as I moved to the music, closed my eyes, and my mind flashed to the summer of grade ten, standing on the logs on Miracle Beach with Kate and Lise, sipping Budweiser, singing at the top of our lungs, "'Cause I'm free, free fallin' …"

Lise and Kate looked over. I knew it was time to go.

⌒

I woke up the next morning to the sun peeking through the curtain. I felt energized and decided to go for a run along the beach. My legs were strong, the sun warmed my face, the salty smell of the sea flooded my senses and I felt lighter.

After four days, we layed on the grass outside Kate's civic, waiting for our return ferry, "Save a Horse, Ride a Cowboy" came on. I cranked the volume and we danced wildly, singing to each other.

The ferry arrived and as the foot passengers unloaded, a tall middle-aged woman with salt and pepper shoulder length hair walked by and commented, "Wow! Cortes Island must be a really fun place." I beamed at Kate and Lise. I had everything I needed.

Katrine Cardew

The Squeaky Door

Do you ever find yourself irritated by little things? Someone clicking a pen? *Click click click.* Or someone jiggling their leg beside you? *Jigigigig.* This is a story about a little thing like that that got under my skin and what happened as a result.

It was back in 2003 when I wintered in San Francisco. I heard about an intriguing workshop happening in the warehouse district at a place called One Taste, Urban Retreat Centre and I decided to check it out.

I entered an anonymous building and walked down a long hall to find a small room at the back stuffed with people. In the middle of the room was a semicircle of empty chairs and along the wall were two long rows of chairs filled with people observing the chairs in the centre. In front of the semicircle sat the founder of One Taste, Nicole Daedone. She had long blown dry hair with gold streams and intelligent brown eyes. She wore tall brown fuck-me boots.

I tentatively took a seat in the centre. After some introductions, the assistants began singling us out and asking very personal questions. "What turns you on? What would it take for you to give up control? Who are you attracted to in this room?" The participants were on the edges of their seats. No one appeared to be breathing. Except Nicole Daedone's assistants, who kept getting up to leave the room. Each time one of them entered or exited the room, they had to open this really squeaky door. A participant would be in the middle of answering one of these very personal questions when, *Squeeeeaaak.*

After a while, I couldn't take it anymore and my hand shot up into the air. "Excuse me!"

Nicole Daedone responded, "Yes."

"May I ask a question?"

"Yes."

"The assistants keep getting up and leaving the room and every time they leave the door squeaks and it's really annoying."

"And your question is …?"

"My question is, is this intentional? Is the squeaky door part of the workshop or are you guys just really *fucking* disorganized?"

"Yes and no. Yes, there are a lot of assistants and they keep getting up and leaving the room and the door squeaks. But if you are waiting for there to be no squeaky door so that you can have your orgasm, you will never have your orgasm. Because there will always be a squeaky door."

I turned red. It was true. There was always a squeaky door in my life. There was always something keeping me from settling down and being comfortable. When I was in San Francisco I missed Vancouver. Medical insurance, walkability. When I was in Vancouver, I missed San Francisco. "Canadians are so boring," I'd complain to other Canadians. So I just kept going back and forth between the two cities, the two countries, never committing to anyone or anything.

And when it came to sex, when it came to my body and how I liked to be touched, I was very particular. I found most men to be incompetent. I was frequently annoyed that I had to tell them what to do.

After the workshop, I went back to Berkeley where I was renting a room in someone's house. It was a bad situation which came to a head after the workshop. One night, I threw my possessions into my minivan and drove away without any idea where I was going. I had been feeling lonely and isolated anyway and decided I wanted to live in a community. Then, I remembered that One Taste had space.

One Taste had a warehouse where people lived with fifty double beds lined up next to each other. Some had curtains between them. Some didn't. Some people had their own beds. Some were paired up as "research partners."

The only space available was right next to the bathroom so talk about squeaky doors. There was actually no door on the bathroom. You could hear the peeing, the flushing. Possessions were crammed onto a few shelves. In the morning you were woken up by the sounds of people packing and unpacking their things. The crunch of plastic bags, the zipping of zippers, the sounds of objects dropping and rolling down along the wooden floor.

I had an anxiety attack just thinking about living there. But I actually had nowhere else to go.

They tried to pair me up with a guy to be my "research partner" but I flatly refused. At $800 a month, I was entitled to my few square feet of privacy. Plus, he wasn't my type.

Every morning at six a.m. a woman wafted through the warehouse singing a gentle song. This was our signal to drag ourselves out of bed and walk next door to the Centre, up a flight of stairs and into a large room where there were two rows of grey scratchy blankets laid out across a hardwood floor. The women lay down on the blankets and the men "OMed" them. "Orgasmic Meditation".

Each woman was partnered with a man. Another man sat in the middle of the room and set a timer for fifteen minutes. "Ready, set, begin stroking." The male partner would stimulate the upper left quadrant of the woman's clitoris. They told us that was where most of the nerve endings were. About six thousand. The whole point was you weren't supposed to have a goal, you weren't supposed to go "over the edge." It wasn't allowed. I had my thing that I did. I would squeeze my legs and my ass to get myself going. But they said no, you have to be totally relaxed.

"Just lay there and receive the stroke however it comes," Nicole Daedone said in her evening lectures. *Just like the squeaky door.* "Accept the stroke. This is the stroke that life is giving you."

I didn't like that I was so particular. Because I've never liked men who were particular. "Do it faster, do it harder ..."

"Do it yourself!" I'd think. "I mean, if you're so clear about how you want it done." It's a creative act for me how I touch someone. I saw my lover as my canvas. I wanted my lover to surrender to me and relish in everything I did, exactly how I did it.

I wanted to be able to give that sense of creative freedom to my lovers. They taught us at One Taste that if you are not appreciating the stroke you are being given, you have three choices: 1. Tolerate it. Say nothing and wait for it to be over; 2. Ask for adjustments—higher, lower, lighter, deeper; or 3. Find pleasure in the stroke exactly as it is coming to you.

The first week was tough. I lay on my grey scratchy blanket in this big room with twenty other women being "OMed" and some of them were very loud. I just lay there quietly, trying my best to "meditate" while wondering if my partner wouldn't rather be OM-ing one of the loud girls.

Afterwards, we would have breakfast together and then we would write in our journals which we were encouraged to share. One woman wrote, "I saw a lavender sky." Another wrote, "I was floating down a river of cream." I wrote, "Didn't feel much. Is there something wrong with me?"

One day, one of the loud girls was assisting. She kneeled down beside me and whispered in my ear. "It's not about coming. It's not about making anything happen. It's about being present to the sensations in your pussy, whatever they may be."

I began to cry. My pussy had never been given the space to just *be*. There had always been an agenda. I always felt I had to perform. I had to get turned on as quickly as possible so that my lover would think I was a good lover.

Each morning I returned to my grey scratchy blanket to try again to feel something. The loud girls coached me. "Breathe into your pussy. Make some sound!" The sounds brought more sensation. First, there was sadness and tears. Feelings of grief which I journaled about. All the times I'd given up my power to men. How I'd used sex to get love and ended up feeling unloveable. And then, as the sadness cleared, I began to feel more pleasurable sensations. Subtle sensations, delicious sensations, profound feelings of joy. One day I saw fluffy clouds. One day I was partnered with a man with flaming red hair and we got high off my pussy and spent the day playing ecstatically in Golden Gate Park. Whenever we came down, he stroked my pussy and we got high again. Finally we made love and I came with no effort at all.

I lived at One Taste for three months and I learned to find the pleasure in every stroke as it came. As I became more turned on, I also took more pleasure in the strokes that life was giving me.

So my question to you is, do you have squeaky doors in your life that are preventing you from having your orgasm? How much pleasure are you receiving from the strokes that life is giving you? And could you ask for adjustments that would allow you to enjoy it even more?

Sara Hansen

Hay and Leather

I love the smell combination of hay and leather. I'm not sure whether it's the mix of the sweet and musky scents or whether it's what that smell represents to me now.

When I first started coming to the Victoria Therapeutic Riding Association (VTRA), I admittedly didn't believe it was therapy. I thought it was something nice people did to bring joy into the lives of people with physical and mental challenges. But I believed it would be a great distraction after this major trauma in my life. I was on the waitlist to get into this association for over a year after a permanently debilitating brain surgery—the wait was worth it.

The stables are located in rural Central Saanich. We park (my dad drives me) in the gravel parking lot. There is a ramp leading to a plain, spacious reception room where students can borrow boots and helmets, and to the mounting platform. This room attaches to a narrow viewing room that looks out to the immense indoor riding ring. A gate on the opposite end leads to an outdoor riding ring. Sharing a wall with the indoor ring are the stables. Each stall in the stables also has a back door, in addition to the front one, where the horse can access an outdoor paddock.

Everyone uses the stirrup-level platform, in the indoor ring, to mount. I first started coming to the association in my wheelchair. I use my walker now. It's almost the same routine to mount. I move the walker as close as I can to the tacked-up horse who is almost touching the platform, use my right hand to grasp the back of the saddle, the instructor moves my walker aside, I then use my left hand to clutch on to the front of the saddle, then not-so-gracefully swing my right leg over to sit. I'm no ballerina but I'm agile enough to do that much.

"It's so nice to see you, Charlie." I pet him on his long, smooth, soft brown neck. "Walk on!"

With that command, he moves forward past the mounting platform. I go large (walk around the ring with him) while the three others get on their horse or they go large while they're waiting for me. Among other things, we practice manoeuvring the horse to weave the line of traffic cones, rehearse guiding the horse in a perfectly straight line (harder than it sounds), using our legs to steer the horse as well as the reins, or practice our two-point over poles laid in the bark mulch. In two-point, the rider comes out of the saddle a couple of inches to a squat, feet in stirrups, the two points supporting all body weight, and move closed fists holding the reins to the horse's neck. This position must be held until the last of the steed's legs are over the poles. Or in advanced riders, the position to go into for jumping

"Keep your eyes ahead, Sara!" yells my instructor. Oh yeah, and you can't look at your horse's next step. Then go outside for a lap or two around the outside rink if the weather's okay.

After a forty-five-minute lesson of using my core to stabilize myself through the cones and doing two-point over poles, my legs are Jell-O and my core muscles are sore. Each rider always has a horse handler. When mounting, and when outside, they hold the rope clipped to the horse's halter. During class it's up to the instructor whether the student's horse remains clipped or unclipped. A rider also begins with two side walkers on the left and right. These are volunteers that hold the rider's saddle; forearm bracing each of the rider's thighs until the rider gets more balance and coordination. One of my side walkers, Jane, was a retired physical therapist (how lucky am I to have that bonus skill set?). She gave me additional exercises while riding (like eyes closed or feet out of stirrups) to challenge my balance. She has the reputation of a drill sergeant, but in a fun way. She "retired" from me and has moved on to help a new student. If a rider does fall off, the side walker is there to catch or, at least, soften the fall. As the rider improves, the side walkers are relieved of their duties, usually one at a time, then the rider only has the horse handler. They let the rider control the direction of the horse.

I have tried many therapies: crystal therapy (strap a vile of a particular crystal to a limb or over an organ to get its healing powers), acupuncture, brainwave optimization (listening to sequences of notes), laser therapy (laser lights directed at my surgery scar for a hour), physical therapy, and horseback riding therapy. The last two therapies are the only ones I haven't given up. I feel that therapeutic riding addresses aspects simultaneously. It goes beyond physical therapy, as it engages me intellectually while I try to master what is being taught. It gives me hope as I become stronger after each session. As well, it provides social interaction and camaraderie with other students/volunteers/instructors. If someone saw us, ignorant of our situation, we would look like just another equestrian class. We might look like novices but on our horse we look "normal".

There is another element I can't explain. Horses seem so intuitive. They listen to what you say and they know how experienced a rider is by how that rider sits in the saddle. If I start taking deep breaths to relax and to sit deeper in the saddle, the horse breathes deeper too. There is a fantastic yet bizarre connection I feel to Charlie. Even my instructor sees the connection. She moves horses and riders around so he's available for me in my lesson. She considers him "my horse". Charlie and I just fit together like puzzle pieces. He listens to my voice instead of my tugs on the reins.

From my saddle I don't see my walker or feel uncoordinated but empowered. Charlie responds to where I want to go and how fast, and he does so with fluidity and grace.

The horses go through a very selective process to be accepted. Each are repeatedly tested for placidity, patience, and gentle nature. This association has twelve horses, each assessed and visited many times before the association commits to them.

Many passionate horse people see the benefits of pairing those with cognitive, physical, and emotional challenges with horses. There are many therapeutic riding associations on the Island and mainland. There is a national association as well as an American one. The VTRA is a charitable organization. It is run by a board, employs only five people and depends on dozens of volunteers. The facility they use is loaned to them on a long term basis. Each student pays a nominal fee for a session (seven to eight lessons), two sessions per rider a year and more if spaces need to be filled. The horses have a break at Christmas and the summer off. The rest of the operating costs are met through fundraisers.

The students range in age from seven to seventy. Jane, who has been in most every session with me, is in her seventies. She was in a car accident twenty-five years ago, doesn't have full use of her left limbs and is proof the body never stops healing. I always see her wearing a smile with her riding attire. I hear her Irish lilt as she speaks to KC, her horse. She is an amazing rider.

I have met many incredible people going there. I look forward to hearing what's happened between the weekly lessons: Joan's latest bike trip, Jane's pending trip to Ireland, Liz's (instructor) progression of her first pregnancy and so on.

We're not cantering around the ring but learn very technical aspects of riding, like riding position and to communicate with the horse with our voice and legs, not only the reins. The horse's movements while walking make the rider's hips move like they're walking. Having this twelve hundred pound animal responding to where I want to go makes me forget needing a wheelchair or walking aid. I focus on my posture and riding rather than "seeing" my double vision. Charlie doesn't care about my speech impediment. I am always disappointed when the lesson is over.

I've always had the same time-slot for my lesson—right before Charlie's lunch. I bring an apple or carrot each time, as a thank you to Charlie after class. I used to give it to my horse handler to pass on because his stall is the second to last one. That's a long way for me to walk.

Now I have the strength and stamina to slowly, very slowly, use my walker to get to the end of the barn where his stall is. Giving him a well-deserved treat is a great motivator to practice walking now that I have the endurance. And I want him to know it's from me. On his stall, there is a latch I open to deliver the treat. It swings open, a rounded triangle trough, for me to put the carrot or apple into. Charlie can't get to it until I close the trough. He makes one dip in the container and the piece of produce disappears. He looks at me unblinkingly while he chews, his lower jaw drawing clockwise circles.

"Thank you, Charlie. I'll see you next week."

I start the trek back through the stables to the parking lot. It's only fifty to sixty feet but it takes me about fifteen minutes. I don't mind being so slow. The scent of hay and leather is strongest in here.

Tara Cullis

Old Town: Lax Galts'ap

AN EXCERPT

"Humpback!" Marven's voice interrupted the engine's drone. A vast presence loomed below the water off the starboard bow. I watched it rise to become a small island, its steamy fountain drifting down towards us. Marven shut off the motor and we settled alongside, the Douglas Channel suddenly quiet. My heart pounded. The massive whale was too close—unnervingly bigger than our open boat. It curved forwards. A small dorsal fin rose and slid past; that huge back kept emerging, sliding out of the water. Seconds ticked by. Finally the broad black and white tail rose, signalled, and slid straight down. At last I took a breath. The moist whale-air caught in my throat. Silence. Then Marven revved the engine and off we went, smiling, up the shimmering channel from Hartley Bay towards the ancient home of the Gitga'at.

This trip to Old Town was something of a pilgrimage. In the *adawx*, their sacred history, the Gitga'at recite that thousands of years ago their ancestors came down in a great migration from the upper Skeena, river of mists. As the story goes, at the place where we were headed, between two rich salmon rivers and beside the fertile crab beds of the inlet, the great Blackfish chief *Wah Moodmx* had placed his ceremonial cane, his *ga'at*, to signify the location of their new home, *Lax Galts'ap*. Forever after, they have been known as the Gitga'at, people of the cane.

I was on a journey of my own. I had been invited to record the chief's life story, the story of Johnny Clifton, also known as Chief *Wah Moodmx*—and to discover how this autumn fishing camp of the modern-day people of Hartley Bay fitted into the yearly round of food-gathering. Marven

Robinson, the chief's son-in-law and a Band Councillor well-versed in the ways of the seas, forests, and the white spirit bear, had offered to take me there. I wanted to know what the people gathered or caught here at this time of year and how they processed it, how rich the area was, how dependent the people were on their efforts here and how they lived. And I wanted to know what threats loomed to their way of life. I knew the Enbridge proposal to bring a pipeline to Kitimat at the head of the Douglas Channel, and to send two hundred and twenty-five crude oil tankers per year down the intricate waterway, had struck a chill into every Gitga'at. The people were trying to fight the project. I wanted to understand why.

Half an hour later we swung north into Kitkiata Inlet, traditional home of the Gitga'at people, often called the *Gitga'ata*; I realized the names of the people and the inlet are the same. Marven pointed out the eastern shore, where their petroglyphs still lie. But now he steered cautiously over the shallow estuary. He seemed to be looking for a secret path through the water, an underwater stream that would provide the depth we needed. I was grateful for his local knowledge. It was half-tide so we headed far up the inlet before turning east into the bed of the *Ga'at* or Kitkiata River.

In the distance what looked like a great eagle gradually morphed into Johnny Clifton's white hair and dark jacket, sitting patiently at the prime lookout spot, the edge of the logging bridge over the creek. It was the Blackfish chief *Wah Moodmx* surveying his world. How long had he been waiting? Thinking back over the history of this place, I realized there had been a *Wah Moodmx* on this spot ever since that long migration; that he had been watching three thousand years and more. I had begun to understand what this now small man, sitting in a wheelchair, represented. He might be crippled with arthritis and no longer able to command his boat as he had, in his heyday, through the furies of the Hecate Strait and the high seas; but he was larger than life, a breathing connection to the past and to the future. He waved a welcome and we pulled in under the bridge, amongst the "humpies", the pink salmon schooling at the edge of

75

the river. Just up from the river's edge stood a billowing smokehouse, its clouds scenting the air. Behind it three large new cabins shouldered high bushes aside. Johnny's grey-haired wife Helen emerged in her apron from the nearest door. Her smiling eyes merry, she beckoned us in.

The brass fittings of a large antique stove shone in the middle of the room—the kitchen, smelling of fresh coffee, to its left. I tossed my sleeping bag on one of three single beds for the women lined up to the right—in front of a tent pitched in the far corner: even indoors, Johnny preferred to zipper out the bugs and mice. Above the stove hung a vast rack for drying fish, its wooden slats hiding nearly half the ceiling.

Johnny's great friend and fellow fisherman Archie Dundas appeared, his grizzled face thin and kindly. He took me on a tour of Old Town, starting with the Big House next door, so new it was still scented with cedar shavings. It was larger than the first house, solidly built, its great beams gleaming. Next to that was Archie's own house. A rough path moved upstream past the ruins of older houses. Their beams and posts were now covered in moss and hosts to large trees, the whole hidden by berry bushes. "Fourteen houses were here," said Archie.

Over a welcome mug of coffee, my hosts discussed a group expected tomorrow. "What on earth … a Norwegian film crew? What would they be doing here?" I wondered which story their film would choose to tell. A sad glimpse into a rich but fading past, or the excited documentation of a culture's rebirth? Three new houses: their fresh cedar scent and strong construction insisted that the fourteen houses decaying beside them did not signal defeat.

And so it proved during the next days.

As he sat fanning the smokehouse fire, eyes squinting, Johnny taught me legends of the wolves and the white bear. Helen showed me how to cut and hang the fish overhead to smoke, then how to step on the dried pieces to fit them into their wooden boxes. She showed me where the *moolks* or high-bush cranberries grow, how to stew cockles and bottle coho eggs, how to ferment stink eggs and why you shouldn't. To the fascinated horror of the Norwegian film crew (who luckily had already chosen the positive story), Marven demonstrated how to shoot, gut and butcher a moose right on the spot where Johnny had waved his welcome. After raking out ashes and building the stove fire at seven the last morning, Archie smiled: "Let's go to the 'grocery store'." He took me all the way down the fertile intertidal stretch, pointing out cockles and mussels and Dungeness crabs, life crunching under every step. Geese honked all along the sea's edge; eagles, gulls, and herons surrounded us on the flats, intently watching movement stirring everywhere in the mud and seaweed, as the sun moved out from the mountains towards the eastern entrance to the bay.

Now I understood why the Gitga'at had rebuilt the houses, honouring the wealth of this inlet. But with this knowledge came a new, heart-stopping vulnerability. As I prepared to leave this place, I unexpectedly felt with chest-shrinking angst what the Gitga'at have to lose. In my imagination I heard the tankers' decibels in the distance grow to drown out the mating hums of the plainfin midshipmen, those busy toadfish who sing in the summertime and bark at the crabs, starfish and baby whitespotted greenlings who would prey on their babies hanging papoose-like from the ceiling of their nests. I heard that sound blast into the clouds of rockfish, sea anemones and abalone of every underwater cliff and into the chrysanthemum blooms of squid eggs in every cove. Then, in my mind's eye, I saw the black oil of the first spill coming in on the lapping waves, spreading on the surface, and sinking in viscous lumps to the sea bottom. I saw it move slowly into Kitkiata Inlet. For millennia the ingenious underwater path up the riverbeds had protected the inlet from marauders, but it could be no match for this invasion. I saw the oil touch and gently cover the delicate eyestalks of the crabs as they peered from their hiding places in the mud. I saw it slowly creep over the fat mussels, then fill the holes marking the homes of the sea worms, then the clams. I saw that oil find its way into every frond of the seaweeds, burying them gradually in its thickness, sliding up at last to the creeks themselves, moving inexorably far upriver with the tide until the riverbanks and the schools of humpies were black and motionless. I saw the fire in the smokehouse grow cold.

On the other side of the world, the Norwegians began to re-edit their film.

I raised my head to look out to sea but all I could envision was the seals coming up through the oil, clogging their ears and eyes and fur. I saw the seabirds land on the surface, and their struggle to fight free. And I saw the humpback whale, its keen hearing already blasted by the loudest sounds ever heard in any sea, come up for air—its breathing hole wide open and vulnerable to the oil.

I couldn't breathe.

Speculative and
YA Fiction

Emma Cleary

Sea Monster

I heard about the whale over breakfast at the Railtown Café—April called it "the sea monster." She was eyeing my eggs jealously and poking at her granola with a stained spoon. Since breaking up with Brad over breakfast burritos, she'd found herself suddenly allergic.

"Are you as happy as you could be?" she'd asked him.

He'd moved out of their apartment the next day.

Daily sightings tracked the grey whale as it fed close to shore between English Bay and Siwash Rock. April held her phone in front of my face, scrolled through aerial shots of a whale shape floating in the shallows, like the shadow of a jumbo jet. A barnacled hump breached the surface of the water, clumped with orange lice. "I'm never going on the Aquabus again, Ray," she said, and ordered a side of bacon.

I walked with her alongside the railway tracks, back to her car, then dawdled home to my apartment near Oppenheimer Park. Inside, I dropped my keys on top of the cardboard boxes lining the hallway. I opened the lacquered doors of the closet at the foot of the bed and looked at Brad's shirts hanging next to mine, his neatly folded stack of Levi's jeans. A discarded bathrobe occupied the wicker chair in the corner and the bed-clothes were unmade, a mille feuille of white cotton and yellow chenille. I looked at myself in the gilt mirror, took off my felt hat and coat. Lifted my knitted sweater over my head, messy dark hair spilling over my shoulders. Unzipped my jeans and pulled them down to my ankles, stepping out of them. Stripped off my camisole and underwear. I told the naked woman in the blistered glass three kind stories about my body. Then I dressed again.

A lover once told me the mole on my stomach looked like a beetle. A long black hair grew out of it. It felt unlucky tweezing the hair from the mole. I was too scared to look it up, but what if I died from plucking this hair out of my body? It might leave a tiny hole and disturb the cells in my skin. Make them fester and eat me from the inside out. After that lover, I let the wiry hair grow back. It became my antenna. A feeler to suss out the lovers who'd curse my body with their lips.

＾

During the week, I worked at an insurance office downtown. I used the fire exit at lunch, making sure nobody saw me leave—it'd take me longer than an hour to walk to English Bay and back. I ate my sandwiches sitting on a log on the beach, its dark sand cleaned and raked like a Zen garden. I felt strangely protected in the half-moon bay, beneath the dove-coloured sky. I scanned the gunmetal waves for whale signs—a break in the water, a blowhole—and wondered what April was so afraid of. Grey whales didn't even have teeth; they had baleen plates. They churned up the sea floor, sifting sand for crustaceans. Perhaps you could be caught in that hairy web of baleen, pulled under ocean, crushed. But not swallowed, or eaten. Unless you made yourself so small you could slip down the gullet like a gritty, salty oyster.

Brad and I weren't lovers, not technically, not yet. After the breakup with April, he'd slept on a friend's sofa until I gave him a key to my apartment. We were waiting, our hands and mouths roaming over each other and then rolling away like the tide. I'd lain next to him with my head in the palm of his hand, whispering about what it would be like. "You have cracks," he'd said, his eyes on the fractured ceiling, his fingers tracing soft circles on the inside of my thigh. "I could fix those for you." I'd kissed his shoulder blade, where a wing would grow if he learned to fly.

＾

A message from April woke me at six thirty the next morning: Have you heard from Brad? I told her no. I rolled over onto a cool spot between the sheets and tried to re-enter my dream. Something important had been about to happen.

I snuck out of work at lunchtime again. An upturned sailboat had beached itself on the sand. How whale-like the hull was! A fat shell fell out of the sky and hit the paving ahead of me with a thwack. Buoys clanged out in the bay as the waves shushed against them. I paused at a couple of splashing sounds and eyeballed each barnacle-encrusted rock rising above the waterline. No sign of April's sea monster.

When I got home, I started to make space for Brad's things on my shelves, unpacking his biographies of American presidents, his Stephen Kings. I thought it would be a nice surprise, an olive branch. I knew he was right, that we had to tell April. He was mad at me, ignoring my calls. But I couldn't do it alone. When he came back, we could talk about it calmly. We could start to be together. I wanted him to kiss the mole on my stomach he'd called a beauty spot when he saw it. A beauty spot. Like a view you pulled off the highway to admire, or a river that made you lie down in the sun.

☞

A whale ate me in my dreams on day four. I built a campfire in his belly and lived off the carcass of a seal. I tried not to think about feeding the seals at Fisherman's Wharf as I chewed. After three days, he spat me back out where he'd found me.

I didn't walk to the water at lunch. I ate at my desk while I worked, then left two hours early, telling them I was ill. I went home and began filling in the seams above my bed with putty. My back pocket started to vibrate when I was at the highest rung of the ladder. It was April.

"They found his phone," she said. She was crying.

"What?"

"They found his phone, the police."

I swayed on the ladder. "Brad?"

"He's been missing all week," she said. "He was supposed to pick up the rest of his stuff on Sunday."

I looked at the bookshelf. "No." I shook my head. I almost laughed—I felt a horrible smile pull at the corners of my mouth. "No, it's a mistake," I said. "He can't be missing."

"Ray! Have you seen him? Why are the police asking me about you?"

I dropped the phone onto the bed. Stumbled down the wooden rungs, sank to the floor. I could still hear April, a buzz at the end of the line, calling my name.

⌒

Cracks splintered the ceiling above me like a fractured firmament, my body burrowed in unwashed covers, my beetle belly twitching. I lay curled with my knees against my chest, watching the light play across the wooden floor.

Each time I closed my eyes, I saw Brad in the belly of the grey whale, rekindling the embers of my campfire with a picked-clean seal bone. My eyes flitted between the voids in the room: the shelves I hadn't filled yet with his books, the vacant bathrobe—it was mine, but he'd been wearing it the last time I saw him, the silk tie wrapped around his naked waist—the empty mirror. Maybe we could live together in the belly of a grey whale. As happy as we could be.

Trucks idled in the street below, and a basketball thumped against concrete. I expected the police to call or even come by and hammer at the door of my apartment: *Open up.* Or for Brad to walk in, shrugging out of his jacket, saying, *Hey, did you hear about the whale in English Bay?* Some humdrum mix-up. A cosmic joke. Not swallowed. Not lost.

After dark, I climbed to my feet and stood before the mirror. Unbuttoned my white shirt down to the navel. I touched the small brown dot, waiting. Imagining the murmur of his lips against my skin: "Let me kiss you here, this beauty spot. It's mine now, it's mine."

An ache sharp-edged like hunger gnawed at my gut; the dot wriggled until a coarse black hair shot out and pricked my finger.

My belly rose and fell with the quickening of my breath. Two wiry feelers protruded from the mole, and a dark outer shell hardened over it. Six insect legs lifted the shiny carapace—a jewel of black onyx—out of my skin, then crawled onto the fleshy pad of my index finger. As I carried the beetle to my eye-line, a pair of crystalline wings sprouted in a series of trills and clicks. They thrummed, vibrating the air around me. I confronted the compound eyes, slick like oily rainbow puddles.

The groping antennae traced circles in the air—a feeler, to search out a lover.

I opened the window. I let it fly away.

Nick Clewley

The Weight of Us

THREE EXCERPTS FROM A NOVEL

I talk to empty places now. Bedrooms, grocery stores, neighbourhoods. I tell their unbreathed air about my day, about days that were. And I talk to Norman. The husky doesn't respond, other than the occasional tail wag.

These are ways to keep my voice fit and my brain sharp. Or they're signs that my mind has gone and lost itself.

"Rhys Howell," I say to the Golf and start singing the Pixies' "Where Is My Mind?"

The car windows are down and the wind streams through, raking my hair. Norman sits beside me on the passenger seat. I drift along the highway, over the reflectors in between the lanes, creating a rhythmic series of thuds. I'm south of Lions Bay, heading back to Vancouver. I've driven the Sea to Sky Highway countless times, for appointments with patients and visits with my niece and snowshoeing at Whistler. My surroundings are as they ever were: Winding, cresting roads move from two to four lanes and back to two. The Pacific sits through sparse arbutus trees on one side of the road; blasted rock gives way to a climbing forest on the other. Useless telephone poles run parallel to the highway, which is surrounded by scrub and weeds and dotted with aphotic light standards.

But there weren't always motionless cars.

Or bodies.

This side of the median is relatively clear, but the other side is jammed. I pass through small pockets and clumps of dead traffic. As my headlights hit these vehicles, they reveal the silhouettes of asphyxiated drivers and passengers.

I'm the only thing moving; stillness has overtaken everything else. Norman gazes stoically out the window. Even the ocean has stopped, its whitecaps holding their crests. The August moon waxes overhead, shining a dim spotlight on the scene below it.

It's as though I'm caught in a tragic Ansel Adams photo—one I don't want to be in for another second. This moment has been on my mind for several days, but until now the courage to do it hasn't been there. Or maybe the cowardice to do it.

I don't want to live in this world any longer.

I bring the car to a stop, reach over and push open the passenger side door.

"Time to go, buddy," I say to Norman. I fight the choke in my voice. This big, dumb dog has kept me sane-ish for the last ten days, but it's time to let go. "Come on, hop out." He tilts his head and gives me un-comprehending eyes. I step out of the car and come around the passenger side, take him by the collar and guide him outside. I pull a bag of dog food, his bowl, and water from the back seat and place them on the ground. He chows down when I pour the food in the bowl and ignores me.

"I'm sorry." I wipe the tears from my face. I should have left him in Squamish or Lions Bay, but this moment wasn't with me then, and I can't afford to lose it now. He'll do fine without me. He knows how to live.

I drive off without looking back at him. The road clears; I close my eyes and turn the headlights off.

"One."

My foot leans on the gas pedal and I wait for the feeling of crashing through the barrier.

"Two."

All I feel is the road beneath me.

"Three."

New car smell. Maryanne and I never had a new car.

"Four."

The clutch grinds a little as I slip into third. It's me, not the car.

"Five."

I open my eyes. A light, where it shouldn't be.

⌒

I want to go beyond the blue. To row past the break and see what's out there, over the horizon.

I could do it. Today's water is calm and fine and would make for good rowing.

I'm standing on the edge of our island as the tide nips at my painted toes, while to the north terns and frigate birds fight over a spot to dive for dinner. The winds have passed and the rains have slunk off elsewhere to fill the endless ocean and we're left with calm blue for another season.

I like the winds. I like the salt they bring to my tongue and the way they blow through my long hair. I like the choppy waves that have no-where to break but here on our land of wave and windswept beautiful. I imagine those waves travelling all over the world, looking for us, waiting for a chance to batter our home. I want to follow them all the way around, from here all the way back to here, seeing our same stars from different perspectives and meeting new ocean life.

Emlyn's the one who's most taught me about the stars and the blue and sharks and about near everything. Few years ago when I turned thirteen we were down spear fishing the shallows at Land's End, talking about constellations, and she says on other parts of Earth it's a different sky, that up north you wouldn't be able to see the Southern Cross. I asked her how she knew that, so she got a coconut from the basket and she marked a line around the middle of it with her stone and she tilted the coconut and then she grabbed a white pebble from the sand and held it out a ways from the coconut. She said the coconut was Earth and the pebble was a star. She said because the earth is round that if you're up north or down south you can't see over the horizon and can't see the pebble star. I asked her how she figured that out and she got quiet and said, "People long before me figured that out." It was a bit confusing, but I like knowing new things, so it was clean.

Without much wind coming off the blue, today smells green and grainy. The towering coconut palms at my back lean out, watching over North Sands. Its white sand peaks and valleys from end to end—the softest sand in the world, like the down feathers of a baby tern.

There's a crunch of footsteps behind me, and I turn as Theory approaches. My heart stops to pick up a few hitchhiking beats and my smile fights not to burst. The light catches her starburst hair as she walks toward me.

"Hey, Cloud." She grins.

⌢

The trick was dead and my head felt like it was trying to give birth to a cannonball. I woke up to a room rife with stale sex, and morning sunlight breaking through the plaid curtains of the high basement windows. He—Jerry was the name he gave me—was stomach-down on the bed, wearing nothing but a white button-down shirt and loosened tie. His face had a pallor, as though he had drunkenly put on vampire makeup.

By the time Jerry had come in the night before, I was the only one left working—everyone else had gone home coughing. Jerry wasn't coughing, so we agreed to spend some time together. He paid with American bills, and I shot up before we started. After we finished he asked if he could stay. It was against Maggie's rules for a trick to spend the night, but she wasn't there to enforce them.

Jerry started hacking and gasping during the night, but there was nothing I could do, even if I hadn't been floating. I got him some water, but he broke the glass when he tried to grab it from the side table. The smack Eurydice'd me after that, somewhere deep and hollow, until the morning sun did what Orpheus couldn't and brought me back up.

I avoided the broken glass on the carpet and tried shaking Jerry, but he was stiffer than his cock had been. In muted horror, I picked up my rumpled green pullover dress off the floor and threw it on with a pair of flip-flops. I slung my bag over my shoulder and went back over to him, put my arms underneath him and pulled hard to turn him onto his back. I buttoned his shirt and cinched his tie. It was deep red with ships' anchors. I took the afghan off the couch and draped it over him. It wasn't long enough to cover his length; his feet were left sticking out.

Up the stairs in the parlour all was calm. The front door was open, and the street, normally alive with traffic, was dead. I almost slipped but caught myself. The floor was streaked with massage oil from a tipped-over bottle that lay on the counter. Beside it was a note in my friend Carla's handwriting, addressed to me.

Linny babe, go long and go far. This place is hooped.
xo Carla

It was unlike Carla to be alarmist. I pocketed the note and skirted around the massage oil, out into the deadest afternoon I'd ever seen in Canada's poorest postal code. Wind-blown trash moved across the street. A nineties BMW was parked in front of Maggie's—Jerry's, perhaps—but that wasn't what caught my eye. Double parked on the other side of it was a van the colour of low-grit sandpaper with no windows on the side, one of those kinds you expect kidnappers to drive. Through the tinted passenger window, the silhouette of a man slumped against the steering wheel. I ran over to the driver's-side window and knocked, but dude didn't rouse. I opened the door and retched from the smell that poured out. The guy was wearing a gas mask; his face looked like the inside of a rotten avocado.

I was starting to jones, but I was out. I had cash, so I walked toward Zeb's place in Gastown. Just a little would tide me over enough to stay calm and figure out what to do.

Helen Platts-Johnson
The Fine Art of Living
AN EXCERPT

"Evelyn?"

Is that you, God?

I blink my eyelids open.

White walls. Unbelievably bright fluorescent strip light. Stiff, scratchy sheet pinning me down. If this is heaven, someone really skimped on the design budget.

"How are you feeling?"

Since when do angels wear sensible shoes?

⁀

So here's the thing. I realize now that my "awesome plan" may have contained a couple of key mistakes:

1. Bleach does not actually speed up the process of slitting your wrists. Burns like hell, yes. Makes you scream horror-movie style so your parents come running into the bathroom and find you sprawled out in a heap on the floor, yes.

Speeds up the dying part—no. Thanks for nothing, Internet.

In fact, it turns out, it just, well, *bleaches* your wrists. As in ninety-nine point nine percent germ-free. You could eat your dinner off these babies. *Pizza, anyone?*

2. I believed, having read up extensively on the matter, that there were only two possible outcomes to my little experiment. Either I would die.

Or I wouldn't.

If I did, then at least I would finally be free of this torment and my snot rag of a brother might get the dog he keeps telling me would be so much better than a big sister.

And if I didn't, then I figured my parents would be so overjoyed that they might begin to pay attention. That maybe, just maybe, they might listen. And for once in my life, they might do as I asked.

In my head, the scenario for my rapturous awakening went something a little like this:

"Evelyn, you're awake! Look, Karen, she's awake! There is a God!" Dad rushes to my side and showers me with flowers, trinkets of immeasurable value, and ludicrously fluffy kittens. Meanwhile, Mum weeps with joy in the corner. "We're so sorry, Evelyn. How can we make things better?"

I turn, godlike, to my doting parents and read out my pre-prepared list of *Things they could do to make my life a million times better, starting with:*

"*Let me go to private school like I asked you six months ago! Or, better yet, reverse time and never make me go to high school in the first place!*"

Of course, reality is a funny thing.

☞

"I was wondering when you'd wake up again." A nurse in an overly starched uniform shoves a giant thermometer in my mouth. "Your parents are outside."

"Mm pa-umff?" With my mouth full of plastic, this doesn't come out quite how I'd planned.

Fortunately, my nurse is used to thermometer-speak. "Yep. Been waiting to talk to you."

"Muh few!"

She scribbles a note on a chart and yanks out the thermometer with a pop. "Good. I'll show them in."

☞

"Ach! What's *he* doing here?" I glare at my grotty little brother as the door swings open. He's already got his finger up his nose.

Mum sighs and hands her dripping raincoat to Dad. "We couldn't leave him in the car."

"Sure you could," I say. "Just crack a window."

"He's not a dog, Ev," Dad says.

"You sure about that?" I nod to Trevor as he pulls his finger from his nose and stuffs it in his mouth.

"For God's sake!" Mum grabs a tissue from her handbag and thrusts it in Trevor's direction. "Did you talk to him about proper hospital behaviour at all, Dave?"

"Sorry." Dad shrinks to half his usual size. He's a big guy, my Dad. 6' 2". Stocky. Not when Mum's around. She treats him like one of her nursery school kids. Treats me like one too.

"Let's start this again." She marches up to my tiny hospital bed and pulls my top sheet over my hands. Over my *wrists*. "It's cold in here. Don't want you to get sick."

Dad's next. He folds Mum's coat over the back of a chair and shuffles up to my bed. "Good to see you, Pumpkin. How you doing?" He pats my head with one of his giant bear paw hands, the same way he used to when I was little.

A lump catches in my throat. *If only you could fix everything as easily as you did back then.*

"I see the nurse's got a new trolley," Mum says. "Good she got rid of that squeaky one, it was driving us all mad. Wasn't it, Dave?"

Dad says nothing. Just stares at his shoes as if they're the most fascinating things he's ever seen.

"Ugh, can I sit down? My feet are killing me." Mum takes off one of her stilettos and rubs her foot.

A prickle of unease runs up my spine. *She always wears high heels. Even in Tesco.*

"Didn't you want a cup of coffee, Dave?" Mum's stopped rubbing now. She's eyeballing Dad.

He doesn't answer. He's too busy staring out the window, humming some stupid insurance advert from TV.

"Dave!" Mum throws her shoe across the room.

"What?" Dad jumps so high that, if he were in the Olympics, he'd have won a medal.

"A *coffee*, Dave? You were just saying how you could really *go* for one?" Mum very obviously inclines her head towards Trevor.

Dad's face is blank. "Was I? Oh. *Oh* ..." He reaches into his pocket and pulls out a fistful of change. "Go get your old man a coffee, Trev. And something for yourself from the machine. Whatever you want."

For the first time in eight years, Trevor willingly relinquishes his search for nostril gold. "For real?"

Dad nods.

"Wow!" Trevor snatches the coins and races out the door.

What the heck is going on? Coffee in the middle of the afternoon? Bribing Trevor with vending machine sweets? I throw back my scratchy sheet and pull myself up the bed. "Now listen here—"

"Evelyn, your Dad and I have been talking." Mum puts her stockinged foot down on the floor in one swift motion. "We know you're unhappy."

You do? I open my mouth to speak, but I'm so shocked they've noticed that all that comes out is a deflated wisp of air.

Mum half-turns to Dad. "Something has to be done. Things can't go on like this."

I nod, bobble-headed. Maybe I don't need a list. Maybe I don't need to say anything. Maybe they've finally realised it's time to help me.

"Anyway," Mum continues, "we think you need a break."

A break? I can't believe it. No wonder they sent Trevor off to get sweeties. Eighteen months he was asking for that Lego set, and even after all those extra chores, they *still* only got him the starter pack. Now here am I getting to go on holiday. Perhaps this not-popping-my-clogs thing will turn out for the best after all. I lean forward. "Are you serious?"

Mum nods. "Yes. And we've come to a decision."

A rush of excitement fills my chest. This is it, the day my parents officially become awesome. The day they redeem themselves. This is *my* Lego set. But I'm not settling for a stinking starter pack. I draw a breath deep into my lungs and try to sound calm. "So, where am I going? Paris? Jamaica? An all-inclusive spa retreat …?"

From over by the window, Dad starts tapping his feet.

"Uh, Dave?" Mum shoots him a look.

He stops tapping. Shuffles left, shuffles right. Jeez, it's a full-blown version of Chicago over there.

"Dave!"

"Sorry!" He comes over to my bed. "Um, Evvie?"

"Yeah, Dad?"

He tries to smile but his lips don't quite make it and they're left kind of hovering in some sort of sad limbo.

My heart sinks. I've seen that look a thousand times. It's the one that says, we couldn't get you a puppy but we got you this great goldfish! Or, we know you wanted the pink shoes but all they had left was this boring brown. And, we know your life is ruined but you'll just have to deal with it.

He clears his throat and goes to put his hand on my head. This time, though, I don't let him. He sighs. "Evvie, we're sending you to Primrose Hill Psychiatric Facility."

Ta-da! He might as well have added jazz hands.

Judy Bicep

The Good Ghost

AN EXCERPT

Miss Gerry thought she saw the last of me when she sold me. Took me one hundred and twenty-two years, but I clawed my way back. Back to her big old house. Miss Gerry's long gone. Gone before I could make her pay for what she did to me.

The bones of her house haven't changed. Two storeys, four bedrooms, grand spiral staircase cutting up through the middle. A wide oak front door. Wraparound porch. The horse chestnut and the ginko are still there, but the cherry and plum trees that sheltered Miss Gerry's room are gone.

The stove is new. The telephone is new. The people are new. Their names are Carolyn and Mark. They fell in love with the house. I spied on them when I first arrived. Got myself caught up to date. I know all about computers and Wi-Fi. I can even speak like them.

As a child, I was afraid of ghosts. I thought they could hurt me. Now I'm the ghost, but I won't do anything drastic just yet. I'm not mean. I want to make Miss Gerry pay for the way she treated me. I was her sister—half-sister. Same father, different mothers. My mother worked her thumbs off for them. Our father made Miss Gerry promise that she would take care of me. But as soon as he got all feeble-minded, she marched me off to Mrs Slater. Now, she was mean. She didn't let you have Sundays off. I'm going to settle the score, as they say now. I'll start gently. Maybe with some English ivy. Then move on to mould. Maybe a leak in the basement. Or termites. The new owners won't check, and by the time they do, the damage will be done.

⤳

"Who's there? Mark, are you playing games with me?" Carolyn walks around the kitchen, a jar of pickles in her hand. She stands at the counter and puts pickles on two plates, next to the hot dogs she made.

I stand by the dining table that I used to clean after Miss Gerry ate.

"Mark, you're freaking me out." Carolyn shivers and pulls her cardigan around her.

"Who are you? I know you're there." She walks barefoot across the cold stone tiles toward the dining room. "Come out. Come out before I—" She whirls around and almost trips against the dining table. "Who are you? What are you doing in my house?"

She can see me. Blazes.

"Who are you?" she asks.

I jump like she's caught me stealing quarters from Miss Gerry's change jar. She never counted it, would never know if I helped myself to her loose change.

Carolyn moves closer and puts her hand through me, swishing it around like she's feeling for a spoon in a sink full of soapy water. She isn't afraid of me.

"Don't be shy. You're not the first ghost I've seen." She smiles. "Mark, where are you? Come meet—What's your name?"

Does she think we can be friends? "They called me Emmy, but Ma named me—"

"Come meet Emmy. She looks like she's from the nineteenth century."

He comes downstairs from their bedroom, his slippers clapping against the wooden stairs. "Hot dogs for dinner again?"

"We have a ghost," she says, like she's announcing the winner of the church raffle.

"Carolyn, seriously." His voice is deep and slow, like my father's.

"I haven't seen a ghost since I was six. I thought I'd lost the ability."

Crumbs from his hot dog drop on the carpet as he walks into the dining room. "You're hallucinating from your insomnia. Take a sleeping pill." He sounds like he wants to nod off.

"I can't. Pills can hurt Gabriel."

"You chose a name already? Don't I have a say in this?"

She's with child. She's a bit old to be a first-time mother.

"You're not doing the hard labour," she says. "I think I know who she is."

"The ghost I can't see?"

"Yeah. She's tall and bony and she's got a scarf wrapped around her head. Maybe she worked here a long time ago."

"You could have warned me I was moving into a haunted house before we signed the deed." He frowns and puts down the last bite of the hot dog. "What's that noise?"

"Just the wind. I forgot to close the office window upstairs. Don't worry, honey, I'm sure she won't bang the furniture around. Or hurt us. She looks harmless." She shouts the last part and then laughs.

I like her deep belly laugh.

"Woo-woo!" She goes to one of the boxes in the living room. "I'm gonna dig out the CDs. Put on some ragtime. Make her feel at home."

"You're in my home. Don't think you can be my friend," I tell her. She doesn't listen and puts on "The Entertainer."

No, I won't listen and get swept up again. That time is gone. I go upstairs to the balcony where I used to hide, sneaking time for myself.

Later that night, she comes and sits next to me. "Why did you come back here?" she asks.

"I have business that needs taking care of." I hope that makes me sound like a mysterious and dangerous ghost, but she doesn't flinch. "I want what's mine," I tell her. "This house is mine. I paid for it with my life."

She cradles her teacup. She hasn't taken a sip yet. The night wind blows her hair. She leans over the railing and looks down at the garden. "The English ivy is taking over. It's strangling the rhododendrons."

Does she know I encouraged the ivy to take hold in the garden?

She bites her nails. "I'll look you up, Emmy. I'll find out who you really are. I know someone who can get rid of ghosts. Just in case you're thinking of turning mean." She goes to her bedroom and locks the door.

She's just like Miss Gerry. She thinks she can get rid of me. Bring on the psychics and the séances and the mediums. I want Miss Gerry to hurt like she hurt me. I want her to lose her house like I lost my place in the world. She loved this house more than she loved anyone. She'd step up on the dining table and polish the crystals on the chandelier. She didn't trust me to do it. She understood the house when it talked. She knew there was rot in the ceiling tiles before the handyman could see the mould. She smelled the squirrels who built a nest in the attic. She heard the raccoons trotting around the roof and she shot them with her daddy's gun. But now that I'm dead, the playing field is finally fair. No, better than fair.

"They turned our home into a real-estate asset."

C. Bruce Johnson

The Numinous Waning Season

She was almost at the cabin when something struck the windshield, leaving behind a large messy red patch on the glass. Evie blinked, hit the wipers, and refocused on the road, trying to block out the nausea.

Her phone buzzed. She checked the screen: it was the clinic. Again. She ignored it. A minute later, it rang again. This time it was her mother. Evie sighed and held the phone up to her ear, tucking it under her bandana. "Mom," she said.

"Evie, *where are you?* Dr Fisher called and said you missed your appointment, and—"

"Look, Mom," said Evie, "I'm fine, everything's fine, I just can't …" *Go back*, she wanted to say.

But her mother was still talking. "—trying to reschedule, but you won't answer, and—"

Evie ended the call. When it rang again seconds later, she held down the power button, feeling a guilt-laden frisson of satisfaction as the screen went dark, and buried it in the bottom of her purse.

Thwack. She caught a glimpse of it this time, a small shape that hit the glass and then bounced up and over the car. I don't remember there being any cicadas out here, she thought.

Twenty minutes later, she was at the cabin. She'd booked it earlier that day while pulled over on the side of the highway. The resort attendant had known exactly which cabin she was talking about—surrounded by trees, near the hiking trails and the lake—even though she'd had to

99

describe it from a twenty-year-old memory.

As she was unloading her few belongings, an old man approached the car from the dirt trail that wound its way through the resort. "I'm Newt. We talked on the phone," he said, shaking her hand. "This the one?"

"I think so," said Evie. She leaned against her car—she was dizzy and out of breath, but the smell of the forest was invigorating. "I only came here once, and it was a long time ago, but it looks familiar. I needed to get out of the city, and I thought it'd be nice to revisit—" She broke off as a puff of air tickled her cheek and a bluish shape flew past her face. "What *is* that?"

Newt raised a grey-streaked eyebrow. "Never seen one before?" he asked.

"Seen one what?"

The man chuckled. He extended his arm and cupped his hand upward. "Watch," he said. "They're real curious."

Whatever it was returned briefly, fluttering toward Newt's hand and then zipping away. Evie thought it was a hummingbird, it looked bright blue and moved so fast, but the shape wasn't quite right, the wings were too long. She started to move toward it, but Newt said quietly, "Wait."

It approached slowly, barely the size of a tennis ball: a tiny but unmistakably female figure, clothed in a shimmering azure-coloured dress, with long blonde hair draping down in front of two incandescent emerald wings that sparkled in the sun. They stopped beating as the creature alighted on the man's fingers.

Newt grinned. "Can't believe you never seen a fairy before."

Stunned, Evie watched it take tentative steps along his wrinkled palm. God, it looks just like a person, a little lady, she thought. Its face was bright, its minuscule features impossibly delicate. It was smiling, its expression one of wonder. It reached out a tiny hand and gently poked one of Newt's curved fingers. It seemed to giggle, and Evie heard a sound like the tinkle of chimes. It's beautiful, she thought.

Then Newt said, "They're a goddamned pain in the ass this time of year," and squeezed his fist. From his clenched hand came the tiniest of screams, like a distant baby's cry, but it cut off abruptly, terribly. He opened his hand and looked with incidental interest at the carnage. Thin strands of red and grey covered his palm, and one bent, broken wing fluttered weakly against his thumb. He wiped the mess on the thigh of his jeans, a crimson smear marking the blue denim.

Evie stared at him, silent with horror, but he misinterpreted her expression. "I know, I know—I should have mentioned it over the phone," he said. "Fairy season. It's why you were able to get the place so cheap."

After Newt left, she stood inside the cabin with her back against the front door, holding her head. Was this a gag? The old man hadn't seemed like a creep. "What the fuck is going on?" she asked no one.

Later, she drove into town for supplies. In the checkout line at the grocery store, she saw a sign reading PIXIE-B-GONE—20% OFF. Next to it were aerosol cans adorned with cartoon fairies, their eyes black xs, their faces blue and grimacing. "Is this some kind of sick joke?" she asked the teenage girl at the till.

The girl blinked at her. "Nope—it's a great deal. They're *terrible* bad this year. See?" She pointed to a stack of newspapers; the headline read "Worst Fairy Season in Decades: Global Warming the Cause?" Evie picked up a copy while the girl scanned her groceries. "You know they can get through most any window screens? They'll make a mess of your kitchen if you let …" She trailed off.

Evie turned to see one fluttering behind her. It looked so real: there were no strings, and the way it moved, flitting up and down, back and forth, seemed preternatural.

"Don't move," the girl hissed, creeping around the counter and grabbing a can from the display.

Evie tried to say something, but a wave of dizziness made the floor ripple and she staggered against the till. She managed to whisper, "Please don't—" But it was too late.

"Gotcha!" the girl cried as spray jetted out of the can. The fairy dropped immediately and hit the floor. It tried to stand, then fell on all fours and vomited a teeny stream of black bile before collapsing on its back. Its limbs shuddered and grew still. "See?" the girl said. "It really works!"

Evie closed her eyes for a moment, then asked, "Is there a phone here I can use?" She didn't think she could handle turning on her phone. The idea of all the messages that would be waiting for her made her stomach lurch.

She made the call from the employee lounge. Her mother answered. "Hello?"

"It's me. I have to ask you something."

"Evie! Why won't you answer—"

"*Listen.* And I'm not crazy. But …" She took a deep breath. "Are fairies real?"

A pause. "What's this about?"

"Just, *please*, answer the question."

Her mother spoke cautiously. "Don't you remember the summer when you turned nine? That terrible vacation we spent in that dusty old cabin? We went through half a dozen fly swatters in a single week. Filthy things, like *vermin*, getting into everything. I can't believe you don't remember. Now tell me when you want to schedule your next—"

Evie hung up.

The image of fly swatters, bloody and broken, tugged at her mind, not quite coalescing. The nurses had warned her about "chemo brain," cognitive issues following treatment. Was that it? Or did any of her medications cause memory loss? She tried to remember the fine print, all those side effects. She was only twenty-nine years old. It was so goddamned unfair. How could she have lived most of her three decades without knowing that fairies were real? Or worse, how could she have forgotten something like that?

At the cabin, she was putting away her groceries when something tapped on the window. One of them hovered outside the glass. It wore a long purple gown, and in its tiny hands it held a bent, broken wing.

Evie slowly walked over and opened the window, staring impassively as the winged creature fluttered inside. It flew slowly over to the kitchen table and landed on the rim of a drinking glass. It was crying.

Its tears made Evie suddenly furious. She grabbed the newspaper from her groceries, rolled it up, and started to swing—but stopped just shy of the glass. The gust nearly blew over the creature, and it stared up at her reproachfully. Evie locked eyes with it, raised her hand again, then lowered it. She sighed.

"What do you eat, anyway?" She unrolled the newspaper and scanned the article on the front page. "Anything sweet. Like milk and honey. Okay."

From the fridge, she retrieved the small carton of coffee cream she'd just put away and poured half of it into a bowl. She added a spoonful of sugar and slid the bowl across the table. "Here," she said softly.

The fairy stared at her, then jumped down to the tabletop. It carefully put down the broken wing and began scooping up the liquid with its hands, tasting the mixture. It looked at Evie and smiled.

Another one entered through the open window, zooming past Evie's face and landing on the table. Two more flew in. Within minutes, a dozen were crowded around the bowl, and more were flying around above it, all different shades of vibrant hues, a rapidly shifting rainbow that circled the kitchen as they chased each other, laughing and playing. Soon the air was thick with them, a glorious haze of colour that rang loud with their giggling chime laughs.

Evie wiped her eyes, reached into her purse, and took out her phone, turning it on but setting it to silent so it wouldn't interrupt the lovely sound.

Kitty Widjaja

The Garuda Child

AN EXCERPT

Small, dagger-slit eyes peered through a dark hole in the scarred brick wall of the western gate tower of Yisatu village. Beyond the wall, horse hooves and combat boots stomped hard onto the ground, leaving imprints on the fresh earth. The eyes gazed up from the hole, scrutinizing two guards as they received a shipment of food from a sizeable delivery wagon and lugged the crates onto two separate horse-drawn wagons.

Towering over the two guards, a nobleman dressed in fine robes sat high on a sedan chair, which weighed heavily on the shoulders of an array of lowly servants. On his head stood a tall hat with the lord's title, 君 (jūn), boldly crowned in red. "Be sure to acquire everything. We cannot be short even a single grain of rice for the grand event," he commanded. His shrill voice pierced the otherwise peaceful early-morning countryside like a cat stuck in a turbine.

The two guards in charge of the shipment snapped to attention. "Yes, sir!" they said. One of them, a stumpy man, scurried along hauling the wooden crates, while the other, a lean man whose spine curved like the stroke of a calligrapher's brush, began picking up stray bits of food that had fallen on the ground. He then proceeded to sort through the crates and divide the food according to quality between the two wagons.

"You can send the spoiled food to the slums. I doubt those filthy mutts can tell the difference with their un-rrrrefined taste buds," the lord said, snorting and laughing to himself.

There were crates filled with bread, leeks, ginger—the eyes in the wall darted back and forth, following each new load—garlic, rice, oysters, sea urchin, live chickens, eggs. The eyes widened as they fell upon a crate of tantalizing peaches, before receding back into the darkness of the hole.

"Hurry! Get those boxes moving. The Yisatu village must uphold its honour to the Royal Family and the Wei Kingdom Army," the lord squealed.

"Yes, sir!" the two guards yelled, and fumbled to ready their wagons.

The lord pulled out a folded fan and pointed it toward one of the wagons. "When you're done, bring the freshest foods to the Grand Estate," he said, then pointed to the wagon beside it. "The rest can go to the slums."

"Yes, sir!"

The lord whipped the fan open and cooled himself against the creeping humidity. The fan's metallic gold painting of bamboo leaves glimmered in the sunlight. He turned to the western gate, whose archway framed the village interior, and narrowed his eyes at a group of day workers hanging red lanterns in the street. At a slight wag of his finger, his porters began carrying the sedan chair through the archway.

Sweat dripping down his curved back, the lean guard tied his last knot. He circled to the back of his wagon, when a round pink fruit bounced out from behind a crate and rolled under his boot. It smooshed into a slippery paste and he skidded, barrel-rolling ahead.

Thud-thud-umph!

Body twisting, his limbs contorted one way then another, like a frog in a spasm, and with a final thud, he collided head first with the back of the wagon, which shook upon impact. He mumbled, sitting cross-legged with both eyes fixed on the ground.

"Are you all right?" shouted the other guard from afar.

"Yeah, yeah, don't worry about it," he replied, rubbing a swelling lump on his head. As he slowly attempted to lift himself back up, another pink fruit hurtled through the air and smacked him right in the nose. It left behind a wet, sloppy trail from the tip of his nose down to his chin before it plopped onto the ground.

The kneeling guard paused, dumbfounded.

Perched on a crate before him stood a hooded figure flinging bruised peaches overboard the wagon. The figure appeared child sized, barely five feet tall, and severely rawboned. A web of veins bulged on its thin hands as it grabbed a handful of peaches.

"Thief! Halt!" shrieked the guard.

Alerted by his comrade's cry, the stumpy man dropped his reins and waddled into a jog around the rear of the other wagon.

The figure stopped. Turned. A large beak protruded from under its hood. Its bill gaped wide to display bright red gums and sharp, menacing fangs that gnarled and pointed in all directions like those of the Garuda—a legendary mythical creature said to have soared the skies during the Spirit Era long ago.

"Garuda Child!" The lean guard sprang to his feet. Together, the two men made desperate attempts to trap the thief. They spread their arms wide, shuffling sideways, and darted to grab at the thief's cloak, which rippled away in the nick of time.

The hooded figure easily ducked, sidestepped, and evaded the grasp of the now red-faced guards. They slumped forward, gasping heavily. As they took a moment to breathe, the thief took to higher ground and rocketed up a stack of crates.

"Stop moving, you impudent little—"

A small foot conked the stumpy guard on the top of his head before he could finish his sentence. The thief weightlessly leaped from his head to another crate as if lighter than air.

Frustrated, the guard cursed aloud, withdrew a sharp blade from inside his sleeve, and threw it toward the thief's skull. "Gotcha," he said, victorious.

The thief ducked. The knife grazed the string of the mask, which loosened and snapped, revealing the face of a young girl bearing a wide bobcat grin and a flower-like tribal tattoo across her left eye. Holding the mask in one hand, she replied, "I think not." She quickly unravelled her cloak and threw it at the guards, trapping them within its folds.

When they finally managed to untangle themselves, she had vanished, along with her Garuda-faced mask.

⤚

Sybil folded the underside of her shirt up and over her belly, forming a cradle for her things, which rattled about as she scampered through a blanket of overgrown grass on the outskirts of the village. The smell of morning dew still drifted on the air. A Garuda mask dangled by a single thread from her hip, tapping against her bare thigh with each step.

She ran past a crooked sign that read Yisatu Cemetery. All around her, rows upon rows of urns and rectangular stones stood erect in silence, like a miniature city for the dead. Each tombstone appeared identical to the next. She examined each one along the way, paying close attention to the slightest snippets of fracture, indentation, and etching. In her mind she pictured the people they once had been.

She passed many tombstones, some with flowers, others forgotten. They all held a small place in her heart, but only one in particular bore a distinct red mark at the top—the mark of a bodiless grave.

Upon reaching the marked tombstone, Sybil released her grip on her shirt, freeing sticks of incense, matches, and a helping of peaches onto the soft, loamy soil. She knelt before the stone, combed the sticks closer together with her fingers, and began to skewer them into the ground one by one, until there were exactly twenty-eight sticks standing.

She placed three peaches neatly beside the stone and stuffed a remaining one into her pocket.

"Oh no," Sybil gasped. She had forgotten a crucial step in the ritual. She began frantically plucking large handfuls of weeds from among the grasses. "Sorry about that! I'll bring garden scissors next time. Granny Karta wants me at the shop this afternoon, so I'm short on time."

Vernal winds caressed her face and ruffled her hair.

"I know it's a special day, but I promise I'll be back later, okay?"

The winds continued to blow through the flowers surrounding her; they nodded their heads in approval.

"There, good as new! I've brought your favourite. They're fresh ones too. It was an easy steal, you should've seen me," Sybil chuckled. "It's a good thing I'm small for sixteen. The smaller the target, the harder it is to catch!"

She breathed out a long breath and lit the incense. Faint winds brushed against her cheek and carried the smoke up to the skies. A calm emanated from the graveyard.

"Happy birthday, big brother." Sybil bowed before the tombstone, hands to her sides, and pressed her forehead against the warm soil and lush grass. *Is this what hugging you feels like?* she thought to herself.

The tips of the blades swayed with the wind, like ocean waves washing away all her thoughts and concerns. It truly felt as if nothing else existed except for her and the love for her family.

Renée McTavish

On Dance Floors

AN EXCERPT

The dance floor of the B Room is a roiling mass of heated, oblivious flesh writhing under flashing red-gold laser lights as music blasts out of the huge speakers at the foot of the tiny stage. Asra Hartley has no idea what song is playing, nor does she particularly care—her world has narrowed to moving in time with the bass line and drums that thump through skin and bone, wrapping around her heart and squeezing it in time to the beat. This, she thinks, is as about as close to sex in public as it gets. The physical intimacy of all these strangers moving together, subject to the whims of the music and feeding off each other's energy, yet also wonderfully alone—eyes closed, lost in their own heads, in the rush of music, and in their own twisting and undulating bodies. A modern day bacchanal.

On nights like these, beer and shots of Fireball whisky seem unnecessary. But Asra has more than her fair share of both coursing through her system.

It's not about getting drunk, she thinks, it's about being the right amount of drunk. It's a high-wire balancing act that she's been perfecting since she was eighteen—drinking enough to ease the pain of the constant headaches and to chase away the bad dreams, but not enough to be sick later. That fine line has been especially blurry as of late, but in this moment, everything is perfect.

Someone touches her waist, an inquisitive touch of permission. Asra turns and moves toward them, opening her eyes as she goes. He's about a head taller than her, slim, with long, straight dark hair. He's grinning:

playful, impish, and slightly surprised. She grins back, laughs, and steps into his arms. Bass and drums vibrate through both of them as they move together on the dance floor. Asra hooks one arm around his neck and curls the other around his waist. He slips one hand under the thin cotton of her tank top, running his thumb down her spine, taking the time to feel each vertebra on the way down toward the low-slung waist of her jeans. He's still smiling, a take-me-home smile, and with those eyes, black and bottomless in the flashes of red-gold light that play across his face, Asra is damn tempted.

It's not a thing she does a lot—getting these occasional lovers in and out of her apartment discreetly can be problematic, given her nosy neighbours—but fuck it, she thinks. Sometimes it's worth the disapproving stares.

He leans in, his dark hair falling over her shoulder to mingle with her own, and brushes his lips against the sensitive skin just behind her ear. The muscles in her belly and thighs contract with a rush of desire that is nearly painful. His lips press against the outside curve of her ear, and his breath is oddly cool in the overheated club. She shivers, turns her face toward his, skimming her fingertips over his jaw, tilting his mouth in line with her own.

"Asra," he says, "we need to talk."

She's so preoccupied with desire, she almost doesn't hear him. And then it sinks in.

Her name.

From a stranger.

Not good.

She pulls back and he loosens his hold, running his hands up her arms to rest on her shoulders.

"Asra, let me expl—"

Music and blood roar in her ears, drowning the rest of his words in a rush of adrenalin. The sweat clinging to her skin evaporates with a chill that flutters across her entire body.

Asra looks the man squarely in his dark eyes and brings her heel down on his foot as hard as she can, twisting her body as she connects, to cause him as much pain as possible.

He winces, releases her, and she shoves her way through humid air thick with pot smoke and alcohol, through tangles of sweaty bodies still moving to the music. The feel of their skin, the smell of sweat, liquor, and barely contained sex is almost sickening. The spell from earlier is broken. The club is just a loud place full of drunk people, and she wants out. A young man grabs her arm as she tries to pass him.

"Where ya goin', beautiful?" he slurs.

His pupils are completely blown, wall-to-wall black from whatever drugs he's taken. His breath is thick and sticky on her skin as he pulls her toward him.

As his hand closes around her arm, pain blossoms straight up the back of her skull, the ice-pick pain of a migraine, a lightning strike of agony that subsides quickly. But in that moment of pain and vertigo, Asra sees herself on a strange bed, nude, head back and eyes closed, her hair artfully spilled over her bare breasts as he thrusts himself into her, while she gasps and moans with the over-the-top passion of a porn star.

Asra recoils in disgust and shock. What the fuck was that? The young man is swaying on his feet, a greasy smirk on his face. It was him. His thoughts, she thinks. It doesn't make any sense and shouldn't even be possible, but it feels right to her. It feels true. She thinks hard about hitting him—a direct blow to the belly—and then the pleasure of watching that disgusting expression slide right off his face as he doubles over, falls, his face turning scarlet while he struggles to breathe ...

The man opens his mouth to speak, then convulses, bending at the middle like he's been sucker-punched in the gut. He vomits.

Horror and bile creep up the back of Asra's throat and she swallows hard. The people nearest them in the crowd back away a little from the splash of vomit but keep dancing. The man is still holding tightly to her arm, using her to hold himself up while he pukes and gasps. The room wobbles and bends at the edges, and she presses her ice-cold fingertips against her lips to keep from being sick herself.

She looks around, trying to catch sight of the dark-haired man. He's standing just behind a group of young women dancing together, spilling their drinks all over the floor and their feet as they twist and wriggle to the music. His mouth forms the word "wait."

Asra doesn't wait. She pulls the drugged man's hand off her arm, watches him drop to the floor, knees-first into the puddle of fresh bile. Then she turns and bolts for the front door, shoving through the drunken revelers on the dance floor and nearly tripping over the metal doorsill in her hurry to get out. The door shuts behind her and the music inside changes to a dull thumping, which still keeps time with her heart and heralds the return of the ever-present headache.

Outside, there are a few people passing around a joint and others cooling off in the late October air. Two shadows lean against the wall of the club near a Dumpster, burrowing into each other. All Asra can see clearly is a slim stockinged leg with an incongruously large combat boot at the end of it, angled upward, resting high on the hip of the other person. Asra thinks again of the dark-haired man's arms around her, of his lips on her skin, of the capital-L Lust that coursed through her at his touch ... She shakes her head and takes a deep breath.

There is a lone Yellow Cab with its light on, sitting idle at the corner of Kingsway and East 12th. Asra runs to it and climbs in the back, sliding across the faux-leather seat and slamming the door shut behind her. She gives the driver Nana's address in the heart of Kerrisdale rather than her own place nearby. The dark-haired guy might follow her, and there's no way she wants to lead him back to her place now.

She sinks back against the seat as the car pulls away. Did I actually hurt that drugged guy? she wonders. She'd certainly wanted to, and then seeing him fall exactly as she'd envisioned.... And what about what I saw? she thinks. Those sure as hell weren't my thoughts, so they had to be his.

No. You do not have super powers, she tells herself. The guy was drunk and drugged to the tits, of course he puked. As for the dark-haired guy ... just forget it. He might be walking, talking sex appeal, but he's also creepy as fuck.

Asra tries to think about where she might have met him. Maybe at another club on some other night? Given how much time she spends at the B Room, more than a few people there know her name; he could have talked to one of them.

I must have heard him wrong, she thinks. Between the band and the people, it had been pretty loud in the club, and she'd had quite a bit to drink—not to mention the contact high from all the pot smoke. Plus, he *whispered* the words, in a crowded bar no less, so she had to have heard him wrong.

Still, reassure herself as she might, she can't shake the feeling that not only did she hurt the drugged man, she also heard the dark-haired man exactly right.

Asra, we need to talk.

Crystal Soto

Where Have the Kids Gone?

AN EXCERPT

Mother and Father were going out to a movie. That was what they told the kids when the babysitter arrived. After they left, Tommy made machine gun noises as he kicked his feet wildly about. He accidently kicked Sarah in the ribs.

She cried out, "Tommy! You hit me! Stop it! I hate you!"

He laughed, screaming, "Attack the giant from above! Air attack!"

Emma, the babysitter, entered the room to check on them. Her ear was glued to the cordless phone as she tsk-tsked their way.

Later that night when Emma was tucking the kids in, Sarah asked, "Emma, what time will Mommy and Daddy be home?"

Emma shrugged and said to the air as she turned to leave, "You know them, kid. Could be late. Now, don't let the *bed bugs* bite."

Sarah's door creaked open minutes later and Tommy appeared in the doorway. "Are you asleep?" he asked.

Sarah shook her head no. He ran and jumped on top of her pink princess blanket, landing on the foot of her bed. She noticed he held their father's camera. Scared of his answer, she asked, "Why do you have that?"

Tommy had that look on his face. He said, "Let's sneak out and take photos of the stars."

⌒

The air was cold; it pricked at Sarah's string-bean arms. She stumbled over a branch in the dark. Her small hands waving around in front of her, she cried, "Wait, Tommy! Please! I can't see 'nything!"

Tommy had stopped walking. He was standing atop a large hill looking down at something bright. Soft beams of light spilled out through the sparse trees in the distance, lighting a plateau that lay before them. It was much more than a flashlight.

Sarah, watching him, whimpered, "Tommy, I'm scared!"

Her brother made his way down the incline toward the light. He wasn't waiting for her. When he reached the bottom, he laughed and yelled back up to her, "Come on. You can do it!"

Sarah did not move. The hill going down was too big. She was too small. Her feet felt stuck.

The light began to brighten. Tommy walked toward it. The trees were illuminated; she could see moss on them and their dark green leaves—alive. The light began to engulf her brother. He was all but consumed when he turned back, reaching out for her. She stared until he disappeared.

Suddenly, it was dark again. She was alone, and she soon realized how very far from home she was. Her tiny heart pounded in her chest; her little hands shook. She didn't want to leave him. But fear drove her back, back the way they had come. Toward home.

The ground beneath her was harder to walk on. The brush seemed brushier. In the blackness there was a light—no, many small lights. They moved around, searching for her. She knew she needed to get to them. These lights were good. They were far, but not so far.

Falling forward, she called to anyone who might hear, "Help!" Her hands hit the ground with a burning sensation. Someone large came crashing toward her, their light momentarily blinding. He grabbed her arm, and the smell of familiar aftershave overwhelmed her. She knew this man—he was her protector. Sobbing, she called out, "Daddy!"

He scooped her up in his massive hands. They held her so tight she couldn't breathe. His arms were large, muscular, and strong. "Oh, my baby. My angel. Don't you ever, ever, ever do that to me again!"

Her eyes glistening, she told him, "Daddy. Tommy got took in the woods, by the lights."

He stared at her and asked, "Who did?"

⌒

BASE 42

Sarah plays with as many toys as she pleases. Surrounding her are a plethora of plastic things in reds, yellows, blues, and greens. Books to colour in and draw on. Dollies that wear pretty flowered dresses and have long hair. There is a child's bed next to a small night table. The room is whitewashed. Clinical. Dr. Carter scribbles something onto a notepad. She is sitting on a chair watching Sarah play on the other side of a thick two-way mirror.

Sarah says to herself, "They took Tommy, but he'll be back. He always comes to find me. Hide and seek is our game."

The doctor decides to try again. Punching a few numbers into a wall keypad, she waits as the doors slide open. Swoosh. They close behind her.

"Hello, doctor." Sarah says.

"How are you today, Sarah?" Dr. Carter asks.

Sarah smiles and sighs. "I'm okay. I miss my brother."

"Sarah," the doctor says, "Do you recall our discussion about make-believe?"

Sarah sticks out her bottom lip and tells the doctor, "Tommy is real. He is. He had a birthday just last month. He turned five. He's almost two whole years older than me. Tommy loves frogs."

"Sarah, I know you have a very active imagination, but you need to stop the lying. That is what it is when we don't tell the truth. It is a lie. I know you are a very smart little girl who understands that. You have to accept Tommy is not real. I can let you go home to Mommy and Daddy if you do. Wouldn't you like that?" the doctor says, kneeling before her.

Sarah says defiantly, "My brother is real and I do know the difference between a lie and make-believe. I also know you are a bad Doctor Lady and yes I want to go home now."

Defeated, Dr. Carter leaves Sarah alone with her toys. Dr. Malone joins her at the two-way mirror, all long blonde hair and blue eyes. No care or concern, just ice. "How are we doing today?"

"Well, her stress levels are low. She's still determined to hold on to the memory of her brother. I've been unable to remove his presence from her mind. She refuses to let go. I'm not sure how long it will take to convince her that he doesn't exist."

Dr. Malone looks pensive as she says, "I think we might need to get a bit more invasive. Set her up with one of Them. There have been some incredible incidents where they were able to wipe our memories. Let's see what happens. I'm beyond curious. What about the father?"

"I'm certain he'll have no relapses in the future. When interrogated by police, he himself seemed to truly believe he had only one child."

"How long was he subjected to the mind warp?"

Dr. Carter looks through her notes and answers without looking up, "He was with Them here at Base 42 for forty-eight hours."

Dr. Malone looks thoughtful. "What happened to the mother?"

"She comes and goes. She's currently locked up, here actually, on Level 21, I believe. She wasn't so inclined to release the memory of her son, though. It's been seventy-two hours for her and nothing."

"Are they still trying?" Malone asks with a sigh.

"They're trying, but it appears useless." Dr. Carter gives the girl on the other side of the glass a look. One that almost appears remorseful.

⌒

LEVEL 21

The Creature stares at her, its large black eyes like pools of infinity. They are all she can see. The table beneath her fingertips is cold metal. The chair hard plastic.

The Creature burrows, claws, works its way into her mind. She cannot take it anymore; it's been hours, no, days! She whimpers, tries to get up, but cannot move. There is nothing holding her. This room is a tiny prison—a black hole in hell.

Feeling trapped in her own body, she cries out, "I have a son! His name is Thomas James! He was born February 5, 2010. He's five years old. I won't let you take him from me!" She holds tight to the memories of her boy, feeling the thing in her head trying to pull them from her. She screams, "I have a son! His name is Thomas!"

Grace Konn

Einstein Girl

AN EXCERPT

If this had been Earth, Agent Allie Sparks would've reached the extraction point in thirty seconds. But this was 'Trae. With the planet's gravitational force twenty-five percent stronger than that of Earth, it was going to take her at least two minutes to reach her destination. It didn't help that there was a psycho gun-toting Traelin guard catching up to her. Fast.

A lightning arc from the Traelin's gun whizzed past her, narrowly missing her left elbow. She dodged between the indigo cotton trees, her black combat boots squishing through the trail of aqua-blue moss. She touched the zippered pocket on her left bicep, feeling for the hidden data cards to ensure they were still safely tucked away. She had done it! Her first solo retrieval mission.

She dared a quick glance behind her. The Traelin, a short, stocky humanoid in a dark green uniform and headgear, chased her with vigour and agility. As a native to the planet, he was accustomed to 'Trae's greater gravitational pull, while Allie struggled with each step as if she were running through water.

Suddenly her comlink, nestled deep in her right ear canal, buzzed with static.

"Agent Sparks, do you copy? Over."

It was Cora! Transmission from Earth's universe was finally getting through. The wormhole was close.

Another lightning arc zoomed past Allie, and the branch of a nearby tree went up in smoke.

"Sparks!" Cora's voice echoed in her ear. "Wormhole arrival in T minus sixty seconds. Do you copy?"

"Umph!" she muttered. She ducked under a low-lying red-polka-dotted branch to avoid another lightning arc. Ahead there was a clearing where a luminescent ultramarine hole had appeared and was expanding outward.

Her extraction point.

"Allie! Do you copy? You need to be at your extraction point, now!" Cora's shrill voice tickled her ear.

"Copy that," Allie grunted. Another arc struck a cluster of purple trees beside her, sending a flock of rainbow-coloured birds twittering into the luminous green sky.

About five paces ahead, a fallen tree trunk about waist high blocked her path.

"I'll be there in ten seconds!" Allie shouted.

She propelled herself onto the tree trunk and leapt off. Actually it felt more like a hop, but it was enough to give her some height and momentum. She fired on her ankle thrusters and zoomed toward the yawning hole in the middle of the clearing. Behind her the Traelin shouted a high-pitched, nasal scream. A lightning arc flew right above her head and she ducked to avoid it. The arc grazed the top of her helmet with a grinding screech that rattled her teeth. Without the cover of trees, she was an easy target.

She launched into a Superman pose and a few seconds later reached the hole, now a cavernous purple swirl. She shut off her thrusters and free-fell into the pitch black abyss. For the next several seconds, she careened through the silent darkness, her body bobbing up and down as if on a self-propelled roller coaster ride. A pinhole of light appeared, then became a growing disc; it grew larger, until she burst through it, spinning wildly into the zero-gravity universe. A realm of glittering stars engulfed her.

"Welcome home, Allie." Cora's relieved voice resonated in her ear. "Stand by for tractor beam engagement."

Allie's spinning slowed. An invisible magnetic tow rope latched onto her and pulled her toward her base ship, the *Relativity*, orbiting above

Earth. The wormhole doorway closed behind her.

She released her clenched fists.

Nobody and nothing had followed her through.

She slowed her breathing to control the nausea threatening to bubble up her throat. She blinked, then focused on the glittering galaxy and the beautiful blue planet. The view two hundred and fifty kilometres above the earth never failed to amaze and mollify her.

"Cora, when we get back to Earth, I'm treating you to the biggest Plutoccino ever made," she said, referring to the sickly-sweet frozen shake that she couldn't stomach but was Cora's favourite.

"Too bad you're only sixteen. Otherwise, we could have a ..." Cora's voice fizzled into static. The tractor beam suddenly released. Allie flew backwards and started to spin. She fired on her ankle thrusters for control.

Something zipped past her right knee. Then past her left elbow. She twisted to look behind her and gasped. A pulsating, heaving mass of rock particles rushed toward her. It was both eerie and beautiful, each rock moving to its own rhythm but in a collective; it was a synchronized ribbon dancing with ferocious life.

"Holy Einstein!" Allie screamed. In about thirty seconds she was going to be caught up in the most spectacular meteoroid storm she had ever seen. A storm she wasn't going to be able to outmanoeuvre.

Her heart raced. Her black space suit, built with lightweight materials for efficient, aerodynamic galactic travel, would provide no protection against the onslaught. A tiny, sharp-edged micrometeoroid whizzed by her left arm, leaving a small tear in the outermost layer of her sleeve. Fortunately, her skin was still protected by her suit's inner layers. Her chest tightened and she panted for more air. A warning buzz resounded inside her helmet. Her oxygen reserves were dropping faster than normal.

A huge meteoroid torpedoed toward her, its rugged peaks glinting. It was peppered with holes, and in the middle two large indents made for a menacing grimace.

Several lights flashed in her periphery. Out of nowhere, a phaser arc struck the large rock, breaking it into fine dust. A small shuttle sped toward her, firing at more rocks in her vicinity. The shuttle slowed and pulled alongside her, right in the path of several incoming meteoroids. The door slid open and a hand yanked her inside.

She landed hard on the platform. She was startled to see the eyes of Commander O'Neill staring down at her through his helmet. A blaring alarm went off and the shuttle lurched to one side. O'Neill fell backwards. She started to slide out of the shuttle but grabbed one of the handholds just in time. The shuttle swayed and tipped, and her left shoulder smashed against the open door frame. Reaching above her, she smacked the red hatch button. The door abruptly slid closed, but not before catching the flap of her ripped sleeve. With her left arm trapped by the door, she was flung from side to side like a rag doll. Her head banged against the side of her helmet. A loud hiss filled the room as the chamber decompressed. The rocking stabilized and she fell hard to the ground.

"Gravitational sensors and shields are back on line," O'Neill's voice boomed in her ear. He appeared at her side and eased her upright. He pulled out a laser knife and carefully sliced through her sleeve, freeing her from the door. As he ripped the material off her arm, something snapped and flew onto the metal floor with a faint clatter. It was her charm bracelet from Jacqueline, her best friend since childhood.

"Wait, that's Jack's." She reached for it with a shaking hand.

"Leave it," O'Neill commanded, slapping her arm down. He leaned over her and unlatched her helmet, lifting it off her head. He smiled. "Hey, Sparks. Thought we nearly lost you back there," he whispered. He brushed a lock of hair out of her eyes. "Tough as a Mercurian lizard in the heat of solstice."

She tried a weak smile and opened her mouth to speak, but the words wouldn't form.

Then the world went black.

Her head throbbed. A thick wool blanket tickled the underside of her chin. She fluttered her eyes open and moaned.

"Hey, how do you feel?" O'Neill's worried face hovered inches above her.

"Like I've been swimming in an ocean of rocks." She reached up to accept his proffered cup of water as shaky images flooded her mind. "Was the data I retrieved usable? What about that Traelin? He came out of nowhere!"

O'Neill grimaced. "Your mission was compromised. That area was supposed to be clear of guards. I'm downgrading you to Level Two activities until we've done a full analysis."

She choked in mid-swallow. "But I'm Level Four!" Level Two was guard duty at dull diplomatic functions.

"Sparks, don't look so dejected." He smirked. "You might actually enjoy this re-assignment."

She crossed her arms. "Boring dinner dates with the offspring of some bureaucrat? I don't think so."

He chuckled. "There will be some privileged kids, but the environment will be both stimulating and difficult."

Allie whooped and her hands flew up to her mouth. "Omigosh! Is it the Saturn Seven study?" Her heart leapt at the possibility. A position on the biennial scientific mission to review the new settlements on Saturn was a coveted one.

"Uh. Not quite."

"Then where?"

He started to pull something out of his pocket.

She gasped.

"High school," he said, handing her Jack's bracelet.

Alessia Yaworsky

The Business of Dreams

AN EXERPT

It was still early, the sliver of time before dawn. Aaro opened his eyes and reached toward his bedside table. His arm bumped a framed photo of a woman and a small child before he found his wire-rimmed glasses. Swirling dust was caught in a ray of light as it passed through the triangular window above Aaro's bed. Gold, glittering light. He focused on the sloped ceiling, following the pattern of the dark and ancient wood. Lying there, on the edge of sleep, he felt like a part of the house. A fixture. He took a deep breath and exhaled before getting up and dressing for the day's work.

Aaro's feet fell into familiar grooves, socks slipping against weathered wood, as he climbed down the attic steps. He bowed his head through the doorway at the bottom and stepped into his shop.

At the front of the room, a window spanned the shop's entire length. Across the glass were letters, spelled backwards and framed by a shadow of grime: MR SILVER'S DREAMS. Outside, fog hovered over the street, winding its way between the buildings. Worn cobbles stretched across the sidewalk, into the narrow road, and continued across the street where the stores were still closed at this time of day. The cobbles need repair, Aaro noted. I'll have to submit another application to the city.

His thick tweed jacket caught on the corner of a desk holding a small cash register, as he turned his body to squeeze into the centre of the cluttered shop. To his left were two shelves, one labelled Specials and the other Dream of the Week. Directly above, lining the wall, were posters. Faded, corners curling, they showed smiling faces, water parks, endless beaches. To his right, floor-to-ceiling shelves held little wooden boxes, canisters of varying sizes, scrolls of paper, and other trinkets: a bear carved from wood, a snow globe encasing a miniature alpine ski resort, a water-stained set of playing cards, a rusted flask. A life's collection. Hidden away, forgotten.

Aaro stepped into a small kitchen adjacent to the storefront and turned on a kettle. He returned to the store, grabbed a duster from below the counter, and stepped up to a ladder resting against one of the shelves. He was about to ascend and begin his morning routine, when he paused. He tilted his head, listening. When was the last time it was this silent? Aaro thought.

He passed the register and walked through a curtained doorway at the back of the shop, heavy black fabric swimming to either side. The familiar smell of old wood surrounded him. In the darkness, the shelves began to take shape. From floor to ceiling, the towering structures stretched out as if in a vast library, though they weren't housing books. Row upon row of glass jars reflected back at Aaro.

The jars were similar to those used for pickling. They varied in size, and each was marked by a paper label and secured tightly with a swing-top lid and metal clasp. Dawn began to creep in through narrow rectangular windows close to the ceiling. The light illuminated the space to unveil a sea of colour. Each jar encased something different: one held a light and cloud-like substance, blurring from pastel shades of blue to yellow to pink; another contained a thick, molasses-like material that clung to the glass, like slimy chocolate; and another, close to his elbow, was morphing from dark green to light in thick, languorous swirls.

The contents of the jars were usually noisy. As they woke, they would hum or chirp or, on occasion, even yawn. This morning was different. The white noise was replaced by a deeper hush.

Aaro couldn't see anything unusual from this angle. Leaning to one side, he peered around a shelf and further into the space. A gentle whirring began from deeper within the room. He edged along the perimeter, placing each foot down with caution. There, within the far shelves, something. Someone.

Aaro froze. As his eyes adjusted, the figure's silhouette, still shrouded by darkness, began to sharpen into that of a young woman. He watched her: she was focused on something, leaning toward the shelf.

Twice in the past, Aaro had had break-ins. But those had been thieves. They had come in with careless, uninspired hands. This woman wasn't touching anything; the glow cast on her face showed genuine curiosity. Aaro felt a hum of energy close to his ear and turned to look at a jar beside him. Its contents—what appeared to be bright cornflower-blue petals—were hugging one side of the glass as if magnetized by the woman. Along the shelf, the other jars were behaving the same way. They seemed to like her.

And he trusted them.

Aaro knew this shelf well; a sign at end of the aisle was marked Journeys A–C. He watched as she moved closer to a jar. It contained jet-black liquid that looked as if it had a fuzzy texture. Aaro saw that it was shifting within its container, but from this distance he couldn't tell what had entranced the woman so entirely.

A shiver rippled along the shelf, through the contents of the jars. With a quiet flutter, they dipped and dissolved, morphing to form the shape of a face with a high forehead, sharp nose, and widened eyes. The woman's face.

The ebony jar continued to change. Velvet turned to liquid turned to velvet again, and the others followed. Imprinted within them, like branded marks—lighter than their surrounding substances—was a name: Beatrice.

Aaro backed up toward the doorway and reached up for a string pull. Lights began to blink awake. One light triggered another until all the bulbs flickered on, continuing until they were almost lost down the long expanse of the room. The woman met his eyes and froze.

Aaro cleared his throat. "This is private property," he said. He raised his chin to make the words seem more authoritative.

The woman was young, in her early twenties, dressed in formal and strange attire. She wore a midnight-blue dress, which gave off an oily sheen like the feathers of a raven, and was wrapped in a heavy dark-grey cape. Both were tattered along the hem. Her eyes flashed back at him, challenging—the dark blue, almost black, of a starless sky.

She turned and ran. But Aaro knew the large room better than she did and quickly trapped her at the end of an aisle. "Wait," he said. His palms felt clammy. He took in her ragged appearance and saw, around her wrists, what appeared to be raw burns. All of a sudden he didn't know what to say and cleared his throat. "Can I help you?"

She opened her mouth to speak, but nothing came out.

"You—uh—seemed interested in my dreams," he continued, gesturing to the shelves.

The woman's gaze followed his hand. "Dreams?" she replied. Her shoulders released a few inches.

"You've never heard of the Jars?"

The young woman shook her head.

Aaro's eyes crinkled behind his glasses as he smiled. "Oh, well, the Jars, or what's inside them, they're dreams. They're organized by theme, roughly, but you never really know what you're going to get: happiness, sadness, the job of your dreams, the perfect vacation, stormy weather. That's the risk of it. And the excitement." He noticed her tight-set jaw, her concentration.

"How did they know my name? It was spelled out in the jars."

Aaro paused for a moment, looking at his wares and then back at the young woman. "Uh, well, it's complicated. They're quite—real, I guess you could say. And they know things. People. I can tell you more about them, but you look like you could use a cup of tea. I have Earl Grey, orange pekoe, rooibos...." He realized he was rambling.

The woman narrowed her gaze, scanning his face. She hesitated before nodding. "I'm Bea—" She was interrupted by a shrill whistle as the sound of a boiling kettle punctured the air.

"Perfect timing," he said, smiling again.

Bea and Aaro disappeared through the curtains, which draped back around them, dividing the library and storefront once more. The kettle's cry stopped shortly afterwards.

A few minutes later, the shrill whistle began again—but this time it filled the space.

This time, the noise was coming from the jars: they were vibrating, humming, singing.

Alive.

Jocelyne Gregory
All the Dogs Are Dancing
AN EXCERPT

*Twenty years after a Manhattan-sized asteroid crashed
into the earth and caused the Two Years of Darkness,
humanity is scarce and monsters rule. Burner Lee, a teen
from the Wolf Pack of Maine, will fight to protect those he holds dear.*

SUMMER, 20 POST-DARKNESS: OLD TOWN, THE MALL

The sound of a hundred ants marching across the tiled floor echoed
in the empty mall. The back entrance had led me through a long dark
hallway, which opened into a section of the mall where the skylights
streamed light. There were tracks, not barefoot but boot prints. They
disappeared into the supermarket, and I abandoned them.

It wasn't unusual for people to come into the mall and search for
food. They couldn't hunt like Wolves, and they were often too sick or
weak to go after animals. In the autumn, when we wrapped up the salted
fish and smoked meat to take to Quebec, Den Mother would send Fern
to leave some food in the mall before we left.

"Mercy in the dark days," she would say as she prepared the crate.

Sometimes Fern found women and children in the mall. He'd bring
them back to the pack and they would travel with us to Quebec. It only
happened a handful of times, and the last time was nearly four years ago.
If Fern ever saw men, he never brought them back.

Never.

I slipped back inside the shadows and edged along the windows of
the shops. I needed to get to the second floor. The light shining through

the roof and the glass doors was turning a sunset orange. I found the stairs and went up to the second floor, my bare feet hot against the cool tiles. The second floor was a lot like the first floor of the mall—full of useless crap—shoes that fell apart after the first rainfall, pants and shirts and dresses that had rotted away long ago, and jewellery and hats covered in cobwebs, or rusted and ruined.

Except for the one store that wasn't completely useless.

The big black-and-white patterned ball was still there outside the shop's open door. I patted the top of it, leaving my handprint perfectly shaped in the dust. I entered the store. I wasn't interested in what Fern had told me was sports gear, or the clothes, or the useless shoes. I was interested in what was deep in the back. Stepping over the shoes and hats on the floor, I continued until I reached the far back, where the light was dim at best. Shifting through the supplies, I found what I wanted hidden behind a few boxes: a long cardboard box with the image of a net stretched on a large metal frame and people kicking a smaller version of the black and white ball into the net.

Opening the side of the cardboard box, I pulled out the net. It was cloth and metal, and it was strong. I doubted it would rot anytime soon, or get a lobster stuck. Grinning, I tucked it under my arm, but just as I was about to leave, a new sound echoed above the sound of ants endlessly marching.

Sniffing.

I frowned and watched the entrance to the store. Maybe Aaron had followed me, or maybe it was someone else from the pack, or a foreigner. To my surprise, a little rust-coloured puppy waddled into the shop with its nose to the ground. It was following my scent, only distracted twice by the shoes scattered on the floor. I waited until it was at my feet, then reached down and picked it up by the scruff of its neck. Startled, the puppy squealed and started to wiggle like a worm on a fisherman's hook. Its little mouth snapped at me. When we were eye to eye, the puppy stopped and its red ears drooped.

"Can you change back?" I urged.

The puppy's blank look spoke volumes.

"Do you feel that burning buzz in your head?"

The puppy shook its head.

"Look for the burn."

It was getting darker inside the mall, and I guessed it was maybe half an hour till sunset. The puppy yipped, and I put him back on the floor as he began to change. Bones and skin shifted, until a red-headed boy lay in front of me. He was gasping for breath.

"You okay, Riley?" I knelt next to him.

"My back hurts," Riley whined. He struggled to sit up and failed, falling back onto the floor and curling into a ball with his arms wrapped round his head. "My head hurts. Real bad!" The scar where he'd been bitten, right above his hip, was an angry shade of red.

I patted his head. "I know. It gets better." I waited for him to calm before I spoke again. "What are you doing here, Riley?"

Riley sniffed. "Following you and Aaron, but I saw Aaron in the graveyard and he was crying, so I followed your scent cuz I didn't want to bother him."

"You shouldn't have followed us," I warned. "You don't know what could be here."

"I know," Riley sulked.

"You're too young to be on your own, and there are things out there that could hurt you." I had a momentary sense of déjà vu. Was this how Fern felt when I wandered off?

"Like the black pig?" Riley glanced at the store shelves.

"You mean the sow outside?" I was alarmed. Pups stood no chance against a wild pig, especially a sow with young ones. Riley looked up at me; his blue eyes glimmered madly with gold streaks.

"No, the two-legged pig downstairs."

I stared at Riley.

"The two-legged pig?" I said slowly. That couldn't be right.

"The two-legged black pig," Riley corrected. Standing up, he glanced over his shoulder. "I have a tail," he chirped. He began turning in a circle as he tried to catch his red, bushy tail.

Grabbing his arm, I dragged him out of the store. As we left, I tore a faded blue-striped men's shirt off a nearby display and quickly dressed him. People didn't look like black pigs. People wore clothes that stunk of sweat and rot, and were infested with mites and fleas.

Pigs did not walk on two legs.

Riley tried to talk as we descended the stairs, but I shushed him with a vicious hiss. My brain buzzed and my pulse raced. I had to get Riley out of here before the pig found us.

"Burner, look! The black pig!" Riley yelled. Ripping his arm from my grasp, he pointed toward the supermarket entrance.

Indeed, there was a two-legged black pig. It was as tall as me but slimmer in shape. Its skin was shiny, and it had no scent. Its eyes were black and huge, and its snout had a round canister attached to one side.

It stared at us.

"Can we eat it?" Riley chirped.

Slowly, I pushed Riley behind me and passed him the net. "Go find Aaron," I whispered.

The pig tilted its head.

"But Burner," Riley whined.

"Go find Aaron. Now!" I snapped. I stepped forward, my eyes on the pig, while Riley ran for the exit. When I couldn't hear him anymore, I took another step forward.

"Can you change your skin?" The buzz in my brain turned to molten heat. My skin prickled, my muscles twitched. "Are you people?"

The pig tilted its head again, like it was looking behind me, and then I heard them. Boots, whispers, the click of metal, and a long thin *shrink* as an arrow flew past my head and straight at the pig. The pig caught it, and more flew from behind me. One arrow sank into the meat of my right shoulder. I staggered forward as the whispers turned to shouts, and the pig fled toward the supermarket's entrance. Ripping the arrow out of my shoulder, I let the burn in my brain take me.

My muscles shifted and my skin split and stretched. My bones broke and snapped apart before they bound themselves together once more. My brain burned like the centre of the sun. Where it would take a pup an hour to change into their Wolf skin—and many more to change back into their people skin—it took me seconds. The shorts I had worn were on the floor, and in a blur of black fur, I turned to the group.

Five men and two women. A group of Hunters so near our pack! They aimed their weapons at me, but I didn't care. A low growl ripped from my throat.

I couldn't let them leave the mall alive.

Lisa Voisin

Brigid the Amazon

AN EXCERPT

They crept in while I was sleeping.

Their hushed voices and the beams from their flashlights bled into my dreams until the press of cold, bony fingers on my wrists jolted me awake. Before I could scream, a hand clamped across my mouth. Rough fabric was tightened over my eyes, tugging the hair at my temples. I twisted and kicked, but my legs were tangled and useless in my duvet.

"Brigid, don't scream. It's us." I recognized Becky's voice. Her hand lifted from my mouth.

My heart thrashed in my chest. I fought to calm down. I'd been expecting this. "Who's with you?"

The other girl tugged my arms in front of me and bound my wrists. "Shh!" Her breath whistled. "You'll wake your mom."

"You can take the blindfold off, Naomi," I said. "I know it's you. You're hissing through your retainer."

"Shut up!" She slapped my arm. "It's not my fault I've got to wear it every night."

Nobody knew exactly when it would happen, or who would be chosen for the senior prank, but I'd slept in my best pyjamas and bathrobe all week. I'd even worn smudge-proof mascara to bed and tied my hair back into a ponytail, just in case.

"You do know," I said, "that hazing is illegal in most states. Not to mention teen abductions."

"Quit being a drama queen." Becky grabbed my bound wrists and hauled me up. The cold wood floors chilled my bare feet. "You should've thought of that before you came up with this stupid idea in the first place."

"Hey. We all came up with it together. Took a vote, even." The senior prank was a fundraiser for the prom. Two of us, one boy and one girl, would be kidnapped and dragged out in the middle of the night. We took bids, and the top five money-makers were put in a draw.

Looks like I won.

"Come on." Becky pushed me from behind. "Let's go."

⌒

In the school parking lot, Naomi readjusted my slipped blindfold. Then she and Becky guided me out of the car and across the field. Through my slippers, the frozen grass crunched beneath my feet. The crowd murmured, anticipating who it might be. *Surely they'll know it's me.* Perhaps they were just glad it wasn't them.

Naomi and Becky led me up some stairs to a platform and sat me in a squeaky old chair.

"So," a guy's voice said. It was Peter Burchill, Portsmouth's senior class president and chess club champion. "Let's see our first applicant."

Applicant? What was this—a job interview?

Becky snorted. "Don't you mean 'supplicant'?" Maybe chess smarts didn't transfer over to language smarts.

When they took off my blindfold, I expected the field to be lit up like the Super Bowl. Instead, everyone had brought flashlights, candles, and camping lanterns. The field glowed like a cross between a candlelight vigil and a crazed cult gathering. We were probably a bit of both.

The entire senior class sat in the bleachers. A few of them elbowed each other and motioned to the parking lot. I followed the laughter and pointing fingers to see Phil Cavendish and Harry Chalmers from the basketball team dragging in my male counterpart. He was barefoot, with ropes binding his arms. He must have had no idea tonight was the night and had gone to bed wearing nothing but boxer shorts.

There were a few catcalls and whistles as Harry and Phil led him up onto the stage. He was taller than his captors, not to mention wider in the shoulders. His chest was smooth, abs ripped. Though he had a pillowcase over his head, there were only a few guys in school built like that.

When they sat him on the chair beside me and removed his hood, my worst fears were confirmed. It was Logan.

Oh God …

"Burchill, you bastard." Logan's angry breath puffed steam clouds as he spoke. "This wasn't supposed to happen till next week."

Peter laughed, high-pitched and nervous. Nobody messed with Logan. He was undoubtedly the most popular, sweetest guy in school. That was, when he wasn't being dragged out of bed in his shorts in the middle of the night when it was two degrees above freezing. Someone should have tipped him off that he was in the top five, that his name might be drawn, that it would be this week, not next.

Yeah. So why didn't you?

I swallowed back my conscience. Logan was my friend. But he'd been so busy with basketball practice lately, he didn't have time for me anymore.

"You got the lucky draw too, huh?" He smiled, and my mind filled with a rush of not very friend-like thoughts.

"Quit ogling him," Naomi whispered.

I flushed to the tips of my ears and glowered at her, praying he hadn't heard. "I'm not," I mouthed.

"Mmmm-hmm."

"Hey! This is boring! Make them do something!" Some guy from the audience threw a beer can onto the stage.

"Yeah!" a girl's voice yelled. "They should kiss!"

The crowd caught onto the word, chanting, "Kiss, kiss, kiss!" The night filled with the echo of feet hammering the bleachers. Surely someone would complain about the noise.

"Well, it seems we have a request." Peter leered at us. "Logan, are you up to the challenge?"

Logan folded his hands in his lap and swallowed. "Uh …"

"You don't have to do this," I whispered. "Fake it, like we did in drama in the eighth grade. No one'll know."

Peter cupped his hand to his ear and called out to the audience, "I can't hear you, Logan."

"Untie me first." Logan stood, thrusting his wrists at Peter.

Peter sighed and waved for Harry to remove the ropes binding Logan's wrists.

"Don't do it, man," Harry said. "She's huge—it's like kissing a guy."

My cheeks burned. I hated being six feet tall. And I wasn't supermodel skinny either. That kind of tall might be acceptable. But no. I was big tall.

"Hey." Logan shoved Harry. "She's my *friend*. Which is more than I can say for you."

Harry laughed but had to take a few steps back to right himself. "Fag." He stormed off.

Logan locked his green eyes with mine. "Harry's an asshole." He took my hand and drew me to my feet.

I stumbled, almost crashing into him, and had to raise my hand to steady myself.

"Am I going too fast?" The skin of his bare chest was cool and covered in gooseflesh. "I won't do it if you don't want me to."

"No. I …" What was I supposed to say? That I didn't want him to? That I *did*? Standing so close to him made my pulse soar. But I didn't want him to kiss me on a dare, not if he didn't want to.

Behind us, the chanting grew louder. "Kiss! Kiss! Kiss!"

I mock rolled my eyes. "The sooner we get this over with, the sooner you can get back home and warm up."

"Yeah. My nipples are freezing. Not to mention my ass."

I really wished he hadn't mentioned his body parts. Now what was I supposed to think about? It was like saying, "Don't think about a panda! You know, those cute, fuzzy black and white bears? Yeah, now *don't* think about them." Right. A panda. I was kissing a panda, not Logan, the hottest guy in school who was kinda-sorta one of my best friends. Not the guy I'd had a crush on for the last two years.

He closed his eyes and leaned in. When he cupped the sides of my face, the warmth from his hands travelled all the way to my toes. His soft lips pressed against mine, and a rush of heat filled me. I'd dreamt of this moment. Twining my arms around his neck, I kissed him back, and he went for it. He wrapped both his arms around me and pulled me close. Sure, he only did it because of peer pressure, because we were standing in front of an audience in the middle of winter and he just wanted to go home. But to me, it was perfect.

Maybe now he'll see me the way I want him to.

Logan pulled away gently, catching his breath. "That was …"

I blinked up at him. What was he going to say? *Hot? Amazing? Awe-inspiring?*

Then his lips crooked into a grin and he squeezed the outsides of my boyishly wide shoulders. But not in a "that was awesome" way, more like I was his kid sister. His pal. "Thanks for warming me up."

Cynthia Sharp
Marcie of the Stars

Dedicated to David Mai, who continually inspires me

Once upon a time, there was a magical woman named Christine Anderson who yearned to have her own child. She and her husband waited patiently for decades, until they were old enough to be grandparents. For many moons, Grandma and Grandpa Anderson wove their hopes and dreams for a child into a collection of prayers which they kept in a wicker basket on their bedroom windowsill.

One summer night, a mysterious woman appeared outside the entrance of a church bazaar as Christine was leaving. The woman lowered her hood of soft red flannel and called Grandma gently by her first name. "Christine, your wishes have been heard. Keep her in the moonlight," she said, handing her a little doll. She waved her palms over the doll, releasing a swirl of colourful crystal raindrops, then disappeared.

The gift was so precious that Grandma Anderson was very careful with her, keeping her safe at all times and only putting her down on a teensy tea-box bed in the caramel-coloured wicker basket. Soon, the bed had a soother, a soft foam mattress, tiny flannel sheets, and a knitted cover to protect it. The baby doll was adorned with exquisitely shiny clothes, and Grandma carried her everywhere she went, in the pocket above her heart, and placed her lovingly in the basket of prayers at night. This went on for many weeks, the elderly couple sipping their tea and counting the milk bubbles on the surface as blessings of future happiness.

A few weeks later, on August thirteenth, all their wishes came to life. Perhaps it was the full moon shining on the wicker basket, perhaps it was all the chakra light from the crystals in the window, or the magical gems the mysterious woman had placed over the little doll before giving her to Grandma, no one can say for sure, but when Grandma and Grandpa Anderson awoke the next dawn, a baby girl was waiting for them in the basket.

Grandma believed that she dreamed Marcie into being. There was no other way she could explain it. "Marcie of my heart," she called her, for it was as if a tiny piece of her heart had crystallized into Marcie, where it grew and blended with Marcie's own dynamic spirit and being.

Meanwhile, on Otium, in the Yellow Sand Galaxy, a short couple called the Starlights, with sky-blue eyes and soft white hair, sat in an alcove of their honey-coloured stone home, rocking a small child named Zabadon. As they did every night, they told him stories by the hearth, sharing their love and light.

One night, purple and silver bolts crashed through the sky and encircled the entire moon. It was the strongest electrical storm ever recorded in their galactic region. A magnificent royal blue lightning streak crashed through the Starlights' open window and hit Zabadon. It lifted him off his wooden bed and suspended him in mid-air. Electricity raced through his limbs. When the lightning streak finally released him, his magnetic and electrical composition had been altered. With each growing day, the lines of his palms changed like a night sky, moving in the patterns of the heavens. At three years old, Zabadon reached toward objects he wanted and they came to him.

Awed by Zabadon's abilities, the Starlights believed that Stella Pulverem, the Stardust Peace Prophecy, had come true. It was a myth that had been told for generations, that one day a magical being would emerge from the Yellow Sand Galaxy, that he would grow up and meet his Light Bearer twin, and that soon after, Oraculum Paxis, a time of great peace, would manifest. The Starlights lived contentedly until the story of Zabadon's gifts caught the attention of the jealous Princess Amitto.

Princess Amitto was originally from Sandunasia at the southern tip of the Yellow Sand Galaxy, a land where the sea speaks with citizens from their earliest years and where orange, purple, and blue starfish cling to bright rocks at low tide, absorbing the warmth of long summer days. The ocean is held in reverence there, for the people of Sandunasia know that life comes from the sea, that they too emerged from its saline womb. They trust the sea to nurture and guide them, so when they reach their thirteenth year and discover pearls in the large oyster shells the water delivers to the warm shores of the bay, and the aura shining out from the shells onto the teens becomes brightly radiant with the presence of the Light Protectors, the occasion is treated with gratitude and importance. It is said that the pearls reveal a person's calling.

The unhappy princess had missed her pearls and assumed that life didn't have any for her. She grew up in a tiny room and assumed it was why she felt too small. When she was old enough to build her own home, she made her new castle bigger and bigger, telling all the village how it was being extended. Finally, when it was deemed the largest in the land, she opened the door to the marble hall. But something was still missing. So she filled her palace with jewels and prized possessions. Yet still, something was missing.

The something that was missing grew louder and louder inside her, like a little blue voice yelping to get out. So she went as far away from home as she could to get away from the calling she didn't know how to answer. She numbed herself. For a time, she hung out at the Asteroid Aces Café on the edge of the Crystal Galaxy, feeling drawn to music. The Light Protectors hoped she would be touched by the energy of that Seifert Galaxy, but she drifted further and further. Eventually, she interviewed for a job with Apparati Productions, a universal firm whose manufacturing processes were responsible for the deaths of many planets. Amitto climbed their corporate ladder, and though she acquired status and money, she still wasn't fulfilled.

When she heard about Zabadon and saw his abilities with her own eyes, she stole the Stella Pulverem Legend for herself, thinking that if she couldn't be happy or famous for her own talents, maybe she could trick people into believing she was epic. She and her Invidia robots converged on Nocen, the Planet of Machines, where she built a magnetic device strong enough to steal Zabadon away. She sent a chaos of asteroid winds onto Otium, until finally the intensity of the magnetic force lifted the beloved, tiny star child into the evil grasp of her ship, and she whisked him away to Nocen.

There, Zabadon was hidden in a cold cave guarded by cruel Invidia robots controlled by the unhappy princess. Amitto pretended to love Zabadon, but she and her followers tried to suck the life from the star child for themselves. They were jealous of his powers. Amitto claimed the Legend of the Stardust for herself and her male twin, Proditio Pigrum, and they hid the true Stardust Legend away, making him serve them all and hiding his real identity from even himself. If she could convince people that she and Proditio were the prophesied twins of the legend, she thought, maybe then she would feel fulfilled.

Life for Amitto was about what she could get—out of each person, planet and situation—and it was never enough. It never replaced the calling to give from her own true self. She and the lazy Proditio adopted royal titles they knew deep down were not theirs and became lost in intentions of grandeur. They didn't know that they had their own story. What Amitto didn't realize was that the sea always has pearls for all the citizens of Sandunasia many times throughout their lives. Someone had to rescue Zabadon and help Amitto find her pearls.

On her thirteenth birthday, Marcie opened the locket that would answer all her questions, and her Light Bearer adventures began.

Akem

Chakara Tea House

"Ten dollars for the Spirit Guide tea," Perry Chan said. "It's on sale today."

"Are you joking? What was the regular price, then?" Mel said. She craned her neck, attempting to read the blackboard behind him. The teas and their prices were scrawled in neat columns—green teas, black teas, rooibos....

Perry smiled and steepled his hands under his chin. "We serve teas from all over the world." He swept his hand to the side to encompass the large, transparent jars behind him packed with loose leaves and what looked like dried fruit. "We practice fair trade and use ethically sourced ingredients with a low carbon footprint."

"But—" Ten dollars for a mug of tea! That was as unethical as you could get.

"Besides, you're not really here for the tea, are you, Mel-linoe? Consider it an entry fee as well." Perry arched an eyebrow and looked her up and down, taking in her light-pink jacket dripping with rain and her soaked jeans.

"Fine," she muttered, shoving her hood back and shaking out her hair so its wiry black strands haloed her head. She dug her last ten dollars out of her backpack and dropped it on the counter. "Hold the cinnamon."

Perry's hand passed over the money and the till opened like magic. Mel sighed. It was all credit cards from here. She slouched over to the end of the counter to wait for her tea and scope out the patrons of Chakara Tea House. Despite the heavy rain, the Yaletown tea house was filled with the chatter of wet Vancouverites sipping large cups of tea and eating small, expensive snacks that were gone in two bites.

The scents of butterscotch and vanilla floated in the air, making her stomach rumble. The energy she'd received from that morning's canned chicken soup was running out.

She patted her pocket, feeling the memory coin she'd stolen. The coin had to be worth something; rent was past due. She had already used the coin to watch some of the missing ghost's memories, and she was sure she could find him before he became a problem.

Minutes later, her Spirit Guide tea was set in front of her with a friendly smile. "There you go, Mel-linoe," Perry said. "She'll be waiting for you there." He nodded to the front of the store.

Mel followed his gaze. Large bay windows let in gloomy light, illuminating two high-backed chairs that aggressively took up space, separating themselves from their surroundings like an island in the sea of chatter.

She grabbed her tea and wound her way toward the chairs, which were vacant despite the afternoon crowd. A crisp white card with the word RESERVED stood on the low table between them.

She sat and put her backpack at her feet. Her wet jeans stuck to her skin unpleasantly as she sipped the steaming tea. She shuddered at the taste of sand and medicine on her tongue, even as warmth filled her.

"Did you know Vancouver used to be a rainforest?" Madame Morar said.

Mel's teacup rattled in her saucer. She put it down casually as the Spirit Guide shaped herself from smoke in the opposite chair.

"The trees were magnificent giants." Morar lifted her masked face upward, as though she could still see branches of firs and cedars swaying in the sky.

Mel settled back into the chair. The woman did like to make an entrance. "Well, that's why they call it Raincouver!" Mel said brightly.

The wooden mask Morar wore lowered to stare at her with painted eyes. A red, tear-shaped jewel glinted on its cheekbone.

Tough crowd. "I hear you have a ghost problem," Mel said. Small talk wasn't her strong point anyway. "I can handle that for you."

Morar ignored her and looked at the closest table. Mel followed her gaze. A child in a high chair was happily stuffing her mouth with cake beside her baggy-eyed parents.

"Aren't you afraid they'll think you're crazy if they see you talking to yourself?" Morar asked.

"I'm used to it," Mel said. "About the ghost?"

"Which ghost? I oversee all the dead on the West Coast. You'll have to be more specific." Morar traced her finger along the armrest as if she could feel the leather of the chair.

Mel dug out the memory coin from her pocket and held it up between her ring and forefinger. The face minted on the coin was the likeness of the missing ghost, Bobby Ha. Underneath Bobby's face, his dates of birth and death, 1990–2016, curved along the edge of the coin. The flip side revealed a number that counted up the days since his death. He was overdue by twenty-one days.

"Bobby Ha. Twenty-five, and dead for three weeks," Mel said.

Morar's forefinger began tapping on the armrest.

"Seems your Spirit Hunter, Damien, dropped this coin somewhere. Glad I was there to find it." Mel smiled innocently. "Who knows what could have happened if I hadn't been there?" She was certain Damien hadn't told Morar of being robbed earlier today. He'd have looked even more of an incompetent fool than usual.

Morar raised a tanned finger. Mel tensed, ready to run if Morar made a grab for the coin. But she just pressed the tear-shaped jewel in her mask. A column of smoke swirled into being, and the Spirit Hunter appeared, bowing. He straightened, robes flowing as the smoke turned solid. He was tall and skinny, like a coat stand covered in cloth.

Shit. This was unexpected. Mel lowered her hand to her backpack and Chomper stirred sleepily. The backpack was usually inert, but she could activate it when needed.

Damien's eyes glowed green when he saw her. "What is *she* doing here?" he lisped around the coin in his mouth.

Mel couldn't help herself; she made the memory coin dance between her knuckles tauntingly.

Damien lunged through the table, reaching for the coin. Chomper woke with a snarl and grew twice its size, snapping at him. He jerked backwards and his arms windmilled as he tripped over his feet to land on the floor. Mel shook her head. Sometimes she wished more people could see Damien, just for the sheer comic relief.

Morar looked up to the ceiling briefly, then said, "Mel thinks she can get Bobby's ghost before you can."

"For a small fee," Mel added. She grabbed Chomper and reined it back to her side. After a last snarl at Damien with its zipper teeth, the backpack went inert.

"You can't be serious," Damien said.

"After that display, we need all the help we can get, don't you think?" said Morar. "The ghost has eluded you for three weeks. The Judges are bound to notice soon."

Damien pulled himself up and Mel felt his embarrassment almost like it was a physical thing. Oh, well. She said, "My price is a thousand dollars for your wayward ghost." She put the coin in her pocket and Damien's eyes followed it hungrily. "I can get Bobby Ha to you soon."

Morar waved her hand and Damien turned to smoke, dismissed. His glowing green eyes lingered in the air, staring at Mel with hatred before fading away.

"One thousand if you can get this ghost to me before midnight," Morar agreed.

Tonight? That was close. But she could do it. She had to. Mel picked up her backpack and stood. She turned to go, leaving behind the rest of her Spirit Guide tea. What a waste of money.

"Tell me," Morar called after her. "Wouldn't your father be disappointed if he found out you were working for me? He usually hinders the business of death, not helps it."

Mel raised her hood and walked silently toward the door, past the oblivious crowd enjoying their afternoon snacks, and past Perry, who stared at her blandly like meetings with Spirit Hunters and Guides happened every day in his shop. As she shouldered her way out the door, she muttered loud enough for him to hear, "Ethical tea, my ass."

K.H. Lau

Arbutus

AN EXCERPT

A long time ago, the Guild of Dragons was guardian of the Emperor.
The Grand Master, a Yellow Dragon, was head of the Guild;
under him were White Dragon in the West, Red Dragon in the South,
Azure Dragon in the East, and Black Dragon in the North.
Once they had been inducted into the Guild and successfully trained,
the Grand Master would give them supernatural powers:
they could shape-shift into humans and other beings,
make themselves invisible, fly, wield magical powers, and
protect the inhabitants of their assigned jurisdictions with
wisdom, justice, and benevolence.
But they were not infallible.

Tiyin stood outside his cave, on the edge of the highest mountain peak. He closed his eyes and touched the pearl embedded under his chin, a small gold orb ringed by a fiery blaze. "I'm the Grand Master of the Dragons' Guild. I pledge to guard and protect the Emperor and his people with wisdom, justice, and benevolence," he whispered.

With a deep breath, he spread his arms and leapt into the cool summer air. He soared on the light wind like a yellow diamond-shaped kite. He scanned the sprawling mountains around him. They were silent. Satisfied that no one had followed him, he landed on a square plateau. He shuffled toward the centre, his long white beard sweeping the ground as he moved and his yellow banyan robe, sashed at the waist, swishing in the wind.

He stopped when he reached the centre, closed his snake-like eyes and opened his well-seasoned ears to listen for intruders. In the north, hungry baby falcons cried after their mother, who had soared into the sky to look for food. The mother falcon circled stealthily over the valley, before swooping down to strike a surprised rodent and carrying it away dangling from her claws. The light wind crackled and hissed through the crevasses in the interlocked mountains before rushing out into the open air. A little stream tumbled down the steep slopes, carving into the ridges and falling off the ledge it had created; its waters plunged to the base of the mountain and continued to flow, now a full-blown river, across the valley to meet with the ocean in the east. A lone wolf howled on the edge of the western forest, while the trees swayed gently and the bees buzzed among the lilies of the valley. The nightingales sang and a cricket chirped, probably having forgotten that it was now daylight.

Nothing out of the ordinary. Happy, Tiyin opened his eyes and waved one hand, palm out, in a clockwise circular motion. A six-foot-wide golden gong appeared, suspended in mid-air. A smile lit up his deep-lined face as his fingers traced the instrument's hammered surface. It shone in the morning sun, in spite of its age, throwing the rays back onto the dew on grass blades and onto droplets of water hanging on the slopes of nearby mountains.

He took a step back, his hands behind him, and slowly turned to look at the spectacular light show of rainbow colours that bounced back and forth through the air. He nodded, stroked his groomed white beard, and gave a hearty laugh.

There's much to do, he thought. He turned to remove the mallet hanging next to the gong, stretched his arms back, and, with a quick, masterful swing, struck the gong. A low, soulful pitch resonated through the valley, bouncing off the mountain walls and flying through gaps in the mountain ranges. It sped across the land, to be heard only by the being it summoned. Tiyin knew by heart the sound vibrations created by the gong when struck; they were unique to each being, representing their souls, their identities, like the names their parents had given them when they were born.

Tiyin raised the mallet and struck the gong a second time, and again—four times in all. He returned the mallet to its position, stepped back, and waved his hand. The gong vanished.

Soon, Tiyin breathed in familiar blue smoke. It came from the azure dragon, who was travelling quickly but silently, breaking through the wind and leaving behind a thin, bright blue line of smoke in the eastern sky. The dragon glided onto the eastern corner of the plateau. He touched the small azure pearl lodged under his chin and morphed into human form, robed in the purest blue of the sky. He clasped his four-clawed hands and bowed. "Grand Master."

"Meidor, good to see you again," said Tiyin. "Punctual and reliable as always."

"Thank you, Grand Master." Just as Meidor was about to brush his robe and sit on a marble chair, a flaming fireball lit up the southern sky.

"It's Feanix," said Tiyin.

"She's a show-off," Meidor sniggered.

The blazing red dragon sailed down to the southern corner of the plateau, scorching the grass under her feet. Hot on her heels, a flustered black dragon slid onto the plateau's northern edge. Morphing into human forms with a touch on their respective red and black pearls, they bowed. "Grand Master."

"Feanix, Graeca. Welcome," said Tiyin.

"Thank you, Grand Master." Feanix, arranging her fiery red robe, and Graeca, in black, settled into their chairs.

"Why have you summoned us?" Meidor asked, a stream of smoke billowing from his nostrils.

"Still fiery and impatient as ever," said Tiyin. "We'll have to wait for Arbutus."

Graeca chuckled.

"What's so amusing, Graeca?" Meidor scowled.

"That's enough," Tiyin said with a wave of his hand; his patience was wearing thin.

Meidor looked sheepishly away and started to pick at his long, curved nails while Graeca groomed his whiskers.

A lightning bolt of white cloud shot out from the western sky, missed the western corner of the plateau, and slammed into Meidor's chair.

Meidor jumped up and rolled his eyes. "It's only you. Here." He offered Arbutus his hand. "That was quite an entrance, Arbutus."

"Thank you," said Arbutus. Breathless, she quickly morphed into human form. Her flowing robe was of the purest white embroidered silk, and her long black curls were braided with red, green, and blue jewels which complemented her white eyes. "Grand Master." She bowed low with her eyes fixed on the ground. "I'm sorry you have had to wait for me."

"So you should be, Arbutus," said Tiyin. "What's your excuse this time?"

"Small matter, Grand Master. Nothing I couldn't handle."

"We'll leave that for the moment." Tiyin touched the flaming pearl under his chin and whispered, "Aura field." A soft whirring sound spun around the plateau, encapsulating them, making them invisible and inaudible to outsiders.

"I want to remind you of your pledge of loyalty to the Emperor, to govern his kingdom with wisdom, justice, and benevolence. We must not misuse our supernatural powers and divinity. Betrayal is the biggest sin. You know the penalty: incarceration in Oblit, in an orb half your size, and burial in the deep recesses of the earth until you're proven innocent. Do you understand?"

"Yes, Grand Master."

"Now, seeds of discontent have been sown in the Imperial Court." Tiyin's snake-like eyes scanned the four dragons. His brows furrowed. One of them had fidgeted, he thought. "As a result, the Imperial Court is divided into two factions—between the two princes. The Emperor is not happy and he has pointed his finger at the Dragons' Guild."

"This is a serious accusation, Grand Master," said Feanix.

"Did the Emperor mention the name of the culprit?" asked Graeca.

"It's for me to find the truth," said Tiyin. "Arbutus. You tutor the princes. Have you heard anything untoward?"

Arbutus examined her long, slender claws. "No, sir. The usual sibling squabbles. You know—they're young and have a lot to learn yet."

"What were the princes fighting over?" Tiyin asked in a slow, deep voice.

Arbutus hung her head low. *I have to give an answer*, she thought. *They won't go away until I do.* "A game of chess, Grand Master."

"Liar!" roared Tiyin. The sound reverberated around the enclosed aura field. Arbutus squirmed in her chair.

"You knew the rules, yet you chose to play one prince over the other. Why?" asked Tiyin.

Arbutus's mind raced, her breathing quick and shallow. *Who spilled? My rival, Graeco? Except—no, not him. My assistant? Not him.* He did as he was told, as any apprentice would, a loyal and trustworthy one at that, and efficient. She crossed out all the possibilities of who might have pointed the finger at her.

Arbutus sat up straight and stared confidently into Tiyin's blazing gold eyes.

Ken Johns

Lost in Time

AN EXCERPT

John tore his eyes off the countdown clock and turned to his wife. "Ready?"

"No." Sandra fussed with her dress.

"Hang in there." He had to keep her mind off the waiting. "Hard part's almost over."

She blew a wisp of black hair from her eyes. "How do you know? You've never done this before either."

He nodded at the clock. "Thirty seconds to go." A hissing sound drifted up through the grate beneath them.

She huffed out a breath. "Shit."

"Please place one hand on the MCV, Mrs McLeod." The tech in the TSTC labcoat covered the gooseneck mic with his hand while he pointed Sandra at the Miniature Chrono Vehicle hanging between them, as if she somehow couldn't see it.

John smiled. The guy had no idea he was making it worse.

The MCV was the size of a baseball but camo-enhanced, with a touch-screen interface and a holo-projected readout. The translucent red numbers cast a warm light on their faces.

"It's okay, Mom." Jessica smiled through the holo- projection. "We're going to be fine. The Time Squared Travel Company comes highly recommended. I'll see you when we get there."

Sandra gave her daughter a weak smile, but when she turned back to John panic was in her voice. "I don't want to do this anymore."

He touched her shoulder, hoping the warmth from his hand would help calm her. "Are you sure? T minus twenty on the countdown is a helluva time to back out."

"Mom!" Mila glared at Sandra, the faint red glow accentuating her anger. "Quit whining and put your hand on the MCV."

"I'm sorry, Mila." Sandra drew in a quick breath. "I don't think I can do it."

"Fifteen seconds on the clock, ladies, what's it going to be?" John waited for Sandra to suck it up and take the plunge. She usually did, but it had to be her decision.

"Wouldn't you like to go to Venice instead?" Sandra grinned. "My treat?"

Mila rolled her eyes. "I'll make it real simple. I'm going." She looked up at her sister.

Jessica shrugged. "Well, I can't let her go alone. So I guess I'm going too."

That was no surprise. Ever since they'd been kids, Jessica had always backed Mila's plays. Even though they were both adults now, they were still his daughters. He didn't want either of them going without him.

Ten seconds.

Surely Sandra felt the same way. If she didn't, he'd have to step in and somehow stop them from going. Even when it was *her* panic attack, he would have to be the asshole.

Sandra elbowed him. "Put your hand on the damn ball, Sergeant. We're not letting them go alone."

He smiled as he put his hand on the MCV next to hers. "I hoped you might say that."

⤔

The launch room vanished. John's lungs refused to expand. Something collapsed his chest like a fist to the diaphragm. The air pressure pasted his wool shirt to his abs, his back, and his sides, as if he were free-falling in all directions at once. He turned to see how Sandra was doing, but she wasn't there. Everything had gone black, like a cave with no hope of light. He called to her but could not generate a sound. The pressure dropped away from his shirt and he gasped.

The world erupted with light. His eyes closed instinctively, but the purest white shone through his eyelids. Even with his face buried in the crook of his elbow, the light only diminished to a brilliant orange. He waited while it faded to a bearable level.

Uneven ground poked his feet through his thin leather slippers. He opened his eyes. Bluebells? They weren't in New York anymore.

The sea of blue sloped away, covering a meadow about two hundred metres across, surrounded by trees. A single giant oak stood alone in the center; a rutted track led out of the woods and circled it before looping back on itself. From where they stood, a narrow path led down to where regular traffic had trampled the flowers around the tree. The TSTC carriage should have been parked right there. But it wasn't.

The retch of vomiting pierced the silence. He spun to see Sandra on all fours, heaving up her breakfast in the field of blue.

"You okay, babe?"

Sandra wiped the foul drool on the sleeve of her dress before she nodded.

Mila fell to her knees beside her mother. She groaned as she looked up at her sister. "Aren't you feeling it?"

"It wasn't that bad." Jessica spread her legs shoulder-width apart and bent at the hips to stretch.

"Yeah, right." Mila bent over and held her stomach.

"Come on. Just take a few deep breaths." Jessica straightened up, gathering her long blond hair and tying it in a bun. Her hair immediately began to loosen, and she shook it out and tried again. "I don't know what I'm going to do without hair elastics." She offered Mila and Sandra a hand up.

"Don't touch me." Mila struggled to her feet.

Jessica helped her mom up, then put her arm around Mila's shoulders and gave her a squeeze.

"Stop it." Mila pushed the arm away and vomited. Jessica sprang back, avoiding the deluge.

John put a hand on Mila's shoulder. "Are you all right?"

She shrugged it off. "Everybody just back off. I'll be fine, okay?"

John let her be. If Mila said she would be fine, she would be fine. Like most fathers, he had been slow to realize his babies had become grown women and did not want nor appreciate his constant fatherly concern. Jessica had had the good sense to wait until she actually was an adult before gently suggesting his attention might be more appreciated elsewhere. Mila had been of the opinion that she was her own woman by the age of seven.

They all wore loose wool clothes designed specifically to facilitate changing into the period costumes their TSTC guide was to provide. John had on what could only be described as pyjamas, and the ladies wore a front-wrapping thingy with a belt. As Sandra adjusted hers, he enjoyed the view. The fact that the TSTC had not provided undergarments was clearly a bonus. At the age of fifty, Sandra still held a power over him that was as strong as it had been in high school. Her fitness regimen would put most of his recruits to shame, and the result was the hard body of a woman half her age. She undid her belt for the third time, holding the dress open at the front and smoothing the sides toward the center.

"Mom." Mila's eyebrows climbed up under her bangs. "Why don't you just take the whole thing off and prance around the meadow?"

"Okay." Sandra let the dress slip down off her shoulders.

"Mom!" Mila and Jessica squealed in unison.

John laughed. She never tired of teasing her girls. They were still in denial that parents could be sexual beings.

"There's nobody here." She pulled the dress back up.

That snapped him back into the moment. "The guide was supposed to meet us when we arrived." He scanned the forest edge again. "Where is this guy?"

Jessica stepped toward him and looked around the meadow. "It's only been five minutes, give him a chance."

"We're too exposed out here. Let's move up to the woods while we wait."

"Dad. You're spoiling it for everyone." Mila turned her back to him to adjust her dress. "This is supposed to be a holiday, not a manoeuvre."

Sandra touched his arm. "Will you calm down if we move into the trees?"

He tried not to show the true level of his concern, but the training was a part of him. He smiled at his wife and daughters and hoped they would indulge him so he wouldn't have to insist.

"You're so paranoid." Jessica smiled, then started walking up the slope toward the forest.

At least Jess *got it.* As a member of the RCMP, she could understand his concern. Now he just had to convince the other two. He put his arms around their shoulders. "Shall we?"

They followed Jessica but only after registering their protests with a sigh and an eye roll.

John took one last look around the meadow before following his family up the hill. His trousers started to slip, so he reached for the drawstring and tightened it as he walked. He smiled. They looked like they were on their way to the showers.

The searing pain in his thigh ripped the smile off his face.

Sarah Katyi

Only in Belmont Park

AN EXCERPT

"Where are we going?" I followed Adrian's inky outline through an alley between two weathered beachfront condos. Even after living in San Diego all my life, I didn't recognize the area. The transit shortage made exploring difficult.

"You'll see soon enough," he said, continuing his steady gait. I sighed in protest. Whatever secret Adrian was keeping, he wasn't about to share it earlier than necessary.

We emerged onto a wide concrete boardwalk. A low retaining wall separated path from sand, and beyond was the slow lull of the ocean. Shimmering Pacific waves danced beneath a backdrop of moon and stars. A sharp whiff of acrid marine life tempered its magic.

I fell into step beside Adrian and his hand clasped mine, but the quiet of our surroundings made my stomach squirm and flip. Both the path and the beach were empty. A soft, flickering light shone from one window, but nearly all the condos were dark.

A deserted beachfront wasn't unusual, but I hated it nonetheless. Most people had moved inland during the attacks. The old memory made me feel numb. This desolate world was the new normal, the societal rule book erased. My childhood self had never predicted a nighttime stroll with a criminal, but then she had never predicted a decade-long state of emergency, either.

"Cindy?" Adrian whispered my name as a question, a sudden break in the eerie calm.

He tilted his face toward me, but in typical Adrian fashion, his eyes avoided mine. A glare from him could make the strongest of people falter. But what about a glance just between us? For a while now, I'd suspected his reputation to be camouflage, but maybe I'd only imagined the softer side to Adrian.

At my silence, he added, "You're quiet tonight."

Not wanting to share my thoughts, I shrugged and said, "Just taking everything in."

"I'm surprised you're not asking a million questions."

"Your detour caught me off guard." I shot him a pointed glare. "And there's nothing wrong with asking questions."

"So you admit I'm a distraction." He grinned and puffed up his chest to appear grandiose.

"Is there a deflate button somewhere?" Pretending to search, I touched his shoulder and then his neck. He shuddered. My hands withdrew quickly, acting on a will of their own, and fled to the safety of my person. Heat rose to my cheeks. I needed to change the subject. "It's the silence ..."

"It's relaxing?"

"No. Unnerving." I've always hated that feeling of being watched, the prickling of my scalp.

He stopped to face me, but his eyes avoided mine. "What about the scaffolding in La Jolla? I thought you liked quiet."

"No. I said I liked peace. Nature—the view, the breeze, the birds ... No people to get in the way. But this ..." I studied his face. The moonlight cast silver highlights among his chestnut strands. "Night stills everything. Instead of feeling small in comparison to the world, you feel out of place."

"How?"

"Wait for it." I paused. "After the next wave crashes into shore, there's a moment where everything stops. You hear nothing. Time seems to expand."

Adrian looked toward the water. The next wave crested, then collided with the sand with a loud swoosh. The breeze became an inaudible whisper and the crickets muted their chirp. His eyes sparkled with an unearthly brilliance under the night sky and my heartbeat quickened in response. A familiar detachment washed over me. I shook my head, overwhelmed and trying to focus. But just as the moment seemed like it would stretch on forever, it ended. The water surged again, pooling and gurgling, and the breeze carried the tang of salt in the air. The crickets continued their tune.

Adrian exhaled. "You know, I've never noticed that before."

"It's weird, isn't it?" I let out a small, nervous laugh.

"You take the time to see what others miss." He leaned forward and brushed a hand over my shoulder. Even through the cotton of my shirt, I could feel the heat of his touch. I shivered.

He jumped back, just as I had before. Withdrawing both hands, he jabbed them into the front pockets of his chinos. "We should keep moving."

I nodded and continued along the boardwalk. My thoughts raced, once again confronted by two versions of Adrian. The unguarded Adrian—he could be helpful and kind. I liked this Adrian. But there was also criminal Adrian, a forbidding presence associated with terrifying rumours of violence and intimidation.

I cleared my throat and repeated my earlier question. "Where are we going?"

The change in subject released the tension in his posture. He flashed a mischievous smile and clasped his hands together. "It's a surprise, Cindy."

As we crossed Ventura Place, gloomy and deserted Belmont Park came into view. Even from this distance, I spotted signs of dilapidation. Entire sections of the wooden roller coaster were gone. Once an iconic landmark, the Giant Dipper had been transformed during the postwar years into a rotting mess, weathered from salty air and no lacquer.

Adrian's pace quickened as we headed for the gate. This was the surprise? I tried to hide my dismay. It was sweet he remembered, but an unlit, deteriorating theme park seemed like an unpleasant reminder of the past.

White paint peeled off the intricate iron door in strips. Adrian removed the broken padlock and opened the gate. It swung wide with a harsh screech. I followed him to the centre of the park, where he stopped and squared his shoulders. Facing me, he cleared his throat. The shadow of his Adam's apple darted up and down. "The second time we met, you mentioned this place. You said you loved coming here with your parents.

"What you've endured these past few weeks—it's because of me. I know my presence can be ... troublesome." Adrian frowned, then continued, "The least I could do is rekindle a pleasant memory. I know it's not the same, but ..." He shrugged and then motioned a hand signal.

A dizzying array of multicoloured lights sprang to life. I screwed my eyes shut, blinded by the sudden illumination. Even closed, the backs of my lids were tinged red. I forced my eyes open and blinked rapidly. Tears sprang into their corners from pinpricks of pain, but I didn't care. I was mesmerized by the yellows and oranges and blues surrounding me. It had been years since I'd seen so many lights on at once.

I let out a deep, long breath. The annoying, familiar tightness in my chest was gone. I felt ... buoyant. To take in the view, I spun in a slow circle. The boardwalk floor was covered in dirt. Rusty steel doors barred the openings of game booths and concession stands.

And despite the decay, a huge smile spread across my face. Colors flashed in synchronized patterns. Electronic music tinkled and beeped over the sound system. Even in its deadened state, the park oozed a cheerful atmosphere.

"So, what do you think?" Adrian rubbed the back of his neck.

"It's ... I haven't seen this many lights since the war. It's perfect." I grinned and took a step toward him.

He closed the distance between us, so we were almost touching. All my senses felt magnified: attraction entangled by a recognizable tiny, nagging apprehension. I suppressed it. *Keep it simple.*

In a lowered voice, he said, "I wasn't sure you'd like it. I mean, the park's really gone to shit."

I laughed. "True, but it reminds me of a happy time."

"And hopefully creates a new one." A faint blush spread over his cheeks. Emerald eyes locked onto mine. I placed a hand on his waist and pulled him closer. I wanted this kind and compassionate Adrian.

His hand slid around the nape of my neck, thumb lightly tracing the line of my jaw. My skin tingled at his touch and I fought down a shiver, hoping not to break the tension between us. He lowered his head and hot air warmed my cheek. I stood on tiptoe to close the distance.

Adrian pulled back slightly, not to break the embrace but to refuse the kiss. Hesitation glimmered in his eyes. Was he asking for reassurance?

"Kiss me," I said, committing for once.

Leaning forward, he brushed his lips against mine. The touch was delicate at first but quickly grew firm. It tasted of mint and lemongrass tea.

His fingertips skimmed up my spine and almost painfully wove themselves into my hair. I felt my stomach flutter in response. Through Adrian, something primal called out to me.

Unbidden, unease resurfaced in the form of that small, nagging feeling. I had spent so much time debating between two versions of Adrian. But maybe it wasn't just the compassionate Adrian I wanted.

Poetry and
lyric prose

Heather Louise Walmsley

Bounty

Undress yourself of thought. Follow your feet. They will walk you anyway. Your soles spring a new beat on the dirt of this island, Cortes. Peel it off: your fleece of needing-to-please. Here purple grasses sway, long-necked, whim of the wind. Yellow-black bees swoop red thorns, guzzle white petals in simmer and surge of trees. Strip them off: your shorts of shame. Creamy butterfly flutters to drink. Does she think, of the greying edge of her wings? One Maple leaf flaunts wrinkled hide of leather on verge of green. Pert buttercups shine in pride, dripping goblets of molten gold.

She follows her feet. They will walk her anyway, along this tunnel of wild birth, to the opening where Mom and toddler log stand guard. She will shed shirt of guilt, step clean into Smelt Bay. She will walk into a beginning, a vast sprinkling: pebbles and emptied clams, random dog turds, nameless curves of ocean-carved oyster shells, whites of light and pearl and shifting hues of yellows and blues. She will untie her corset of fear. She will suck salt up her nose, expand chest into belly until laces pop from their holes and her breasts hang exposed, nipples stiff and pink like claw of a crab.

I follow my feet. They will walk me anyway, crunch of barnacled rock into ankle-deep mud. I will ditch my shoes, stuck in the warm suck of old lies. Seaweed clutches at rocks, crispy black strings, bloated balloons devil-forked. Five old boulders lean bitter-kneed. I wade shiver of waves, throw my cap of grief into the deep. Fleeing tide unveils a bank of sand dollars and I pull their circles out. My fingers trace shock of pencil-feathered perfect: dragonfly body, two sets of wings, five-pointed star. Divine art.

Cancun

Cancun, village impoverished
strung from the fibre of cactus
infertile soil
spun into rope by Dupont
    see the ghosts of the fisher wives.

City of tourists
dug from the white sand ocean dream
aquamarine
glammed into *Brand of the Decade*
    hear the ghosts of the hotel dead.

City born to serve
breeds a new people   Mexican
Russian Korean
sweat of sixty-seven nations
    hear the ghosts of migrant hope.

City of sickness
wields a scalpel   hips and knees and
plastic faces
bariatric bellies fat laced
    hear the ghosts of unloved chins.

City of healing
boasts blueprints budgets permits for
Wisdom Gardens
a place to *build, research, record*
                    hear the ghost of Chilam Balam.

City of embryos
sucks eggs, ovaries of hot young
fertile local
chicks on a list, height, weight, eye shape
                    hear the ghosts of human love.

City of bodies
disgusting   like the animal
outraged donors
it's a trash   my eggs   so bad pay
                    hear the ghosts of gift exchange.

City of last hope
lures IVF adventurers
lugging sluggish
sperm   barren wombs   white-picket dreams
                    hear the ghosts of stillborn lungs.

City of research
woos me—rich uncharted terrain of
women enslaved—
dangle dictaphone   erase interview into poem
                    wield the ghost of child enchained.

Tree of Between

Your   mammoth   back

shag-robed in green fur
shudders the breeze

knees twist
elbows frisk
dance of rain

legs delve deep
murky mirror dive
edge of Rice Lake

arms stretch high
tantra mudras shape
pulse essence, cloud

trunk
rhizomes air
water, earth

roots, fired in
clay, anchor cosmic

reach   between   worlds

Afterworld

#afterworld

  a time when
wind lifts over
  Desolation Sound

beach shivers with
  creak of splintered trunks
seagull flaps white
  treads tumble of bulbous green

boat births a bush
  cradles life in orange foam, peel of seat
eagle claws flesh
  heaves tongue flop of salmon   ocean to sky

woman stiffens
  rainbows oil   pooling in the sink of her stomach
beetle scuttles
  burrows into vulva   rot of last human, thighs splayed

spirits haunt trees
  wail the freeze between worlds   handcuffed to the grief of it

Ivy Pharness

Wash Cycle No. 1

It's made of steel
couldn't possibly break

so you slam that folly frame
you grab that industrial lever and drive it into fifth gear
like some hellish slot machine
jet streams covet ceramic and plastic
                                eye-rolling restaurant jargon
spin it and spin it
                   for one single minute

our delicate eardrums on the other hand . . .

funny
we could be a deaf nation
and still feel the wind in our hair and upon our ears

see those
whirls of soapy sudsy water in the steely banks
those low basins in kitchenette
                         Page one Martha Stewart's very own Home Ec
so Martha turns around with a devilish grin and her
ear to ear
folded orange jumpsuit
and her pristine linens over bare backed slats

she bakes a key into a cake
a million stainless steel contraptions
ones of convenience
and passing glance
shiny
but bare of function
                        anymore, anyway

the world at our fingertips
dependent on our sense of fragility
we either pound the earth
           or
                      tread lightly

our own sense of fallibility reflects our treatment
of everything else.

run on thoughts

Is my blue your blue? I have to ask myself this continuously as I write. Before I sat down to begin whatever it is this will become I had to mind my seating position my choice of drink and my state of mind. I had to run over a million different thoughts all varying shades of doubtful. Haste finally pointed the gun right at me and gave me little choice. Am I writing out of fear? I am supposed to write but instead I scope out articles about infidelity and the psychology behind innocent "looking" or "admiration of the human form". There's no harm in that. At the end of all my searching I always find myself back at the same conclusion: I can't hold anyone accountable for the things they do, that I also do because after all it is only human nature.

is my blue your blue? When we look up and see that sky, locking us in like ants in a glass dome, we don't really see blue. And looking into our lover's blue, blue eyes we still don't see it. Only when we grab a silly pen and bleed ink onto page do we see the bluest blue our eyes could ever behold. It's like some sick joke.

this morning I thought about my style of thinking. We all have a style of thinking but I don't think we ever frame it as such. We just call it thinking. But in writing or fashion or any form of art we always term it a "style". I am a product of a consciousness and that consciousness is a product of many different things and we all act according to our consciousness. It's a vehicle and not exactly something one manifests. So I can't really blame myself for being what we call "forgetful" or prone to "phobia" even "socially inept". These things derive from something beyond me. There are always things missing and so therefore I need someone else to fill in the blanks, the pot holes or plot holes that happen ,too, of their own accord. How many people does one need to fill all of them in? I need something foolproof, bulletproof, cast in titanium. I need a goddamn political campaign staff, only I won't be affixing a nation's future nor proffering my services for the ultimate glory of my compatriots. I need them for writing punch. I want to churn out enough material to change a goddamn nation through simple clean cut language.

I work in the service industry and it really harkens back to this human insistence that we have other people waiting on us. Some companies really enforce this, they want you to smile and say thank you into oblivion. They want you to accommodate every whim of every customer. It kills me a bit inside each time I help a new person. I only have an allotted amount of time to talk to someone and that is usually during the time they process their debit and credit transactions on Moneris. Let me tell you it's not enough time for meaningful conversation. If I can it is usually a hit or miss. Some people think you're engaging them out of pity or other times it feels contrived and yeah, it is. Sometimes you hit the mark and there is a breakthrough in the flow of conversation exchange and the monetary exchange becomes paled in comparison but that is a rare thing. I think I treat my customers like a mother turtle treats her babies: she births them and then she leaves them in a hole to face the sandy hellish banks of doom until they reach the ocean. And then? Then they face the oceanic depths that contain a myriad of predatory conundrums. The thing is I just have a hard time caring.

Getting back to the colour blue. My mother and father both have green eyes. My father's eyes are more golden and cat like. The green is a bit sinister. My mother's eyes are more like jade, an unforgiving jade that does not dabble in any other shade, does not care to play with hue. When I was born I had the bluest eyes one could fathom. So blue they brought you to that oceanic floor and held you hostage for a bit. As I aged the blue aged too, it mixed with a different crowd, it got grade school art class on me and mixed it's primaries. Now I'm left with some final product of blue green green blue but mostly blue with a little green. My partner has mostly green eyes with a little blue. It's funny what you're left with at the end of the day.

Carole Harmon

Breast Armour

1.
moon snail shell on China Beach
breast shaped creamy white
spirals to nipple
wide red foot
spills from shell
ploughs sand for clams
smothers with muscle

acid etches
while barbed ribbon tongue
seven rows of sharp teeth
drills through shell
slurps and rasps

enzymes pre-cook
juicy flesh within
it takes days

moon snails omnivores   predators
occasional cannibals
as are we

2.
China Beach late October 1997
I've fled mountains, hospitals
failed to halt the inevitable
come to the sea

we were closer
in the autumn of her dying
than all the years of my childhood

my shyness
her impatience
my secrets
her challenge

my
red haired
high heels tip-tapping
index finger wagging
Scottish force of nature
mother

gone

moon snail shell miracle
breast shaped creamy white bulb
spiralling to nipple
better armour
than corsets and bras

Sepia

Italian for cuttlefish
our forgotten ancestor
squid and octopus cousin
swims in shallow southern seas

INK

danger
sepia shoots brown-black
squirts dummy diversions
shape shifts colour
drifts away disguised
bubbles, seaweed, barnacled rock

ink names pigment, tones
photographs with nostalgia

> printing my grandfather's wilderness
> mountains, pack-trains, cowboys, indians
> I spurned romantic sepia
> toned black-and-white photographs
> with value added metal, gold
> traded for silver
> crisp white highlights

SKIN

sepia skin mimics sand, seaweed, coral
cells of red, brown, yellow, black
swell contract   compose colour and form

camouflage sculptures on ocean's floor

leucophores, iridophores glow
iridescent proteins mirror
kaleidoscopes
now you see me   now you don't

females undulate, mesmerize
males dash   iridescent arrows
skin electric

our skin is changeless
our blush can't compare

VISION

it's said we share camera vision with sepia
w-shaped pupils see in black-and-white
twin lenses shift to focus

spectacles correct our single lens
coloured vision
we   black-and-white
audience to sepia's rainbow show

we don warpaint, woad, henna
pierce our skin with tattoos, safety pins
brush Kohl, lipstick, blush, powder on plain faces
weave camouflage
tweed, plaid, herringbone
drape ourselves with polka dots
pin stripes, paisley, cloth of gold,
royal purple, animal skins
emulate our sepia ancestor

ENERGY

sepia ink collected, dried, ground,
diluted, shaken
diluted, shaken
becomes homeopathic
remedy for Eve's sisters, daughters

disillusioned sepia women
clouded with resentment
homebound like snails
feel worn out drudges
drab in dun

rebel sepia women revolt
sheath swathed, high heeled, form fitting
bent on something
defeat the king

balanced sepia women dance
like cephalopod cousins
wave frilly mantles
five sets of arms

      I fall in love with cuttlefish
      imbibing sepia
      long to swim snorkel-less
      in southern seas

we craft words
make and unmake worlds

we cannot return to the sea

Zoe J. Dagneault
Amaranth

Morning:

Magnolia hand at bud dawn
hopeful hours   like little sugar islands

at daybreak   her sentimental beauty
is promise in a mason jar
Dad calls her
his Taffeta Tempest
Dust bowl
Flour bowl
Sugar bowl Queen
she is milk tea & happiness
though people seem to notice
"the bloom of her bread"
her kitchen fills
with pastel pawns
macaroon petals
peach melba
other things   that crumble
"What comes before hope …" she sighs
smiling and spinning
through similar rooms
her charm separates
like cream by late morning

Afternoon:

out back of Buyer's Bog
between mallard bleats
reed wind
swelter heat

Little is knee deep in warm mud
dark as chocolate cake batter
her almond crinoline turns icing
under eggcream Sunday best

inside the house today
air unbearable
hot with hibiscus and baby fever

"Well bless your heart …" Little murmurs
practicing a not yet candied drawl
of her mother's sucrose charm

On her way home   she collects
fledgling debris:
button
shell casing
frog leg
stone

Evening:

        littered in adult sound
        glass and metal

                       consumption
                         clink

        jingle jangle
        jargon jungle
            of main room

                words glint & stretch
                 as diamond branch

            friends & slim lipped rivals
            beg hollyhock contentions

               Mama's eyes set
            for tea party hurricane
       serves bourbon creme brulee & cool
              looks

Outside:
        makeshift coyotes paw
            gold holstered filament

Inside:
        Dad crows "That dog don't hunt ..."
         Mama's laugh
                like sugar cubes
                    in an empty cup

Holstered Planets

his holstered planets   her degrees of
morning
her venture sap
   rubyribs   his riverrun

his hard line   her pristine fraction

                  shadow branch
                  landscape pallet
                  frost armour
                  copper thoughts
                  pine vessel
his pale night looks   her strands of breath
his aching matches

              her arched
                 flicker

her willingness
the ease of his darkness

                  teeming silver creeks
                  his waterrun

                     her sound for him
                     the way he shapes
                       her

her holstered blink
the bloom in her breaking

        her willingness
        in ease of his darkness
            his colour scheme

his thick wit

                the shape of her leaves

                  the shift in her

                    hip

        low glory thump
        hot ache

          timber thin obsession

broken branches
his promise of damage

her frayed winks   his drawn corners

      her road philosophy

      her groundswell

Donna May Cross
It Was a Perfect Fall Day

I shut off the auger, put the grain box down, turn off my truck. One more load of flax is in the bin. We are combining our last field, and it is one of those perfect fall days—enough warmth in the air to heat a person, but still an aftertaste of the cold the night before. As I head up to the house yard for a quick break, I feel relief. Yes, we are going to get through harvest. Yes, we are going to get our fall work done before more bad weather sets in. Yes, my aging father and I have managed to complete another farm season together. And yes, soon I can let the responsibility of harvest slip off my shoulders so I can focus on what's uppermost in my mind: my impending divorce and how I can help my children through the unfamiliar terrain in which we have been mired.

Walking past the trimmed caragana hedge that delineates the division between house and barnyard, I glimpse my two-year-old son playing in the sandbox. Do you know how sometimes when you want to see something clearer you squint a little? Well, just then my heart squinted. For a moment I am taken back ten years, and I am seeing my eldest son playing in just the same way in that same sandbox.

"Mom!" he calls to me, stepping carefully over the side of the box and then barreling towards me as fast as his short legs can carry him—a master of the ungainly but surprisingly fast gait of an exuberant toddler. As he gets closer, I crouch down in a squat and open my arms. He propels his body right into my chest, never breaking stride, never for one instant doubting that I will catch him. As I hold onto him, the center of my life, my marriage, my farm, and my family, a feeling of deep contentment permeates through me. Here, in my arms, is the living embodiment of my happy life. My joy in holding him, pressing my face against his hair, breathing in the dusty, soapy smell of him is a reflection of how I feel towards my whole life—a life filled with love for my husband, my family, and my farm.

"Look," he says, and drags me towards the sandbox, proudly showing me his latest masterpiece of packed sand and muddy water.

I close my eyes then, and a wave of warm emotion washes over me, like a ray of sunshine reviving my body after months of dreary clouds. I savour this innocent, Garden of Eden happiness that has never been tainted by tragedy or loss. Like those warm summer days, it had been impossible not to take it for granted.

My heart blinks then, and my current life snaps back into focus. Gone is my contentment with my well-ordered life. My eldest son is dead, killed swiftly and surely by a brain tumour at eleven years of age. The child at the sandbox now is my youngest son, his little life marred by the tragedy of his brother's death, and the subsequent departure of his father from our home. Yet the absolute wonder in my child is still there. The deep, deep love I feel for my children is even stronger than the love my younger self knew. In my former life, I had always felt the smallest whisper of incredulity. Did I really deserve to have such a good life? And answering myself quickly so as not to let any doubt arise, *yes, of course, because I'm a good person.* Now, there is a sense of surety in my happiness in my child. I feel the same love for my child, for all my children, as I always have, but now there is a sense of reality to it that was not there before. I love them, and I know that love is stronger than death. If I can wrestle some happiness out of this world I am living in now, then that happiness is mine to keep. I do not have to ask if I am worthy of it, because I know happiness is not something you earn, but something you create.

As I approach the sandbox, a little breeze stirs up, and I feel the same unburdening that the right breeze on the right day has instilled in me all my life. It lifts a weight off my shoulders, and I can feel it flowing away from me, my inner eye watching it go calmly, and with a sense of rightness.

My son turns to me and says, "Hi, Mom," with that same cheekiness and those same twinkling eyes that greeted me ten years ago.

"Hi, Sweetheart," I respond, and send a quick little thank you skywards, in the same direction as my earlier burdens had flown, for all that is good in my life.

Jan Klimas
Cold City

It's cold, super cold here
there's nobody around
despite the thousand faces
crowding shops and streets
there's no one to talk to
no one to listen

everybody's busy
chasing their own tails
mowing their own lawns
cooking their own meals
living their own lives
the rest of us are left
to mind our own business

"Hello, how are you"
Hope you're doing well.
"Okay, great, I've gotta go."
What they mean is:
"I don't care."
"Do you, care?"
just spit it out

this city is a dark forest
where malicious creatures hide
they want to walk alone
eat with laptops and iPhones
plug ears with earphones
that shut the voices of real people

as cold as a tundra, an iceberg
too high to climb on
a slippery, dangerous mountain
that lacks human touch

but why?

If we all like living here so much
why do we ignore the coldness
ignore the ignorance
maybe big cities are doomed to stay this way
cosmopolitan

Feeling Old

Eaten bread is forgotten.
And crumbled into past.
Memories like red strings
show us the way back to who
we were and what made us
the way we are today.

"You're not old," I wanted to say to him.
But then I remembered
when I thought I was old.
And everything was lost.
My life as I knew it—lost.
It happened when he was born.
Time slowed down and sped up.
It slowed down because my hobbies were now second priority.

Time flew because suddenly I had no time.
All my time was filled with taking care of my son.
I had come to terms with the feeling of loss and helplessness.
I sympathized with him and wanted to say
"It's gonna be OK."
But then I remembered
the times I felt frightened to death as the rider
on a dark horse
galloped closer and closer to me.

The feeling never really went away.
"Just don't dwell on it. For it cannot be changed,"
Mr Clock-master said.

Bitter King

The king was sour
he was king of lemons after all
but he was ignored by his lazy servants
who grew on the lemon tree

Their juices fermented, almost alcoholic
from hanging on the tree for long
the king shouted:
"Get down you autumn babies!"
"Fall down from the tree you lazy biscuits!"
But they didn't listen to him and
enjoyed the sweet chit chat

His strength was fading
he used to be a firm leader
with thousands of followers among the citruses
now his fan numbers are down
his tweets lagged
his social networks shrank

To reach out to new audiences,
he moved from a lemon to an orange tree
hoping to find fruit he could rule and manage
but
no one listened to him
he was a king of lemons after all

Ice Cream Queen

Don't look at me!
I'm not your enemy!
I'm just too busy to eat you
too busy to even think of you
your soft, creamy delight
hidden in a place where
it shouldn't be stored

if the great powers of the law find out
they will stick me behind bars
separate me from my creamy queen
stored inappropriately

I shall tell them
"please take me but save the queen
she hasn't done anything wrong
except for being mine and
that's not wrong"

The poor thing
she must be terrified now
is she going to be removed from my safe-keeping
is someone else going to eat her
she will melt if that happens
and all her beautiful colours
will spill on the floor

Adriane Giberson

The Story Wrangler

AN EXCERPT

A lone woman walked the shoreline with her dog on a leash. Rosa heard a stomach rumble. Smiling, she looked at Carly and asked, "Was that yours or mine?"

"I can't tell," giggled Carly.

Rosa reached into her pouch and pulled out a pair of granola bars wrapped in foil. "This'll keep us until we get back. Then we can have a proper lunch."

"Thank you," said Carly as she took a bite. "Mmmm … this is good."

"Made it myself," said Rosa as they set off toward the trail. On their downward trek Carly looked on in wonder as Rosa pulled out little handfuls of seeds from a plastic bag, leaving little piles atop shorn down tree trunks.

"What's that for?" asked Carly.

"They're my little offerings to the forest," replied Rosa as they watched a chipmunk flit over to the stump and pick through the pile for a sunflower seed. Songbirds darted over and pecked at the tiny millet grains.

Once they were back in the studio, Carly emptied the contents of her pockets onto the table.

"I think we have enough stuff to draw now, grandma," said Carly.

"I think you're right," said Rosa. "You hungry yet?"

Carly nodded then went over to the wall to hang up her coat on one of the hooks. Rosa had already slipped off her poncho and leaned her walking stick up against the wall. Next to the stick on a hook was a coiled lasso. Though it had been quite a while since Rosa had last put it to use, even as she looked at it now, it appeared to glisten like a shimmering snake, ready for use.

"What's that?" asked Carly, pointing to the lasso.

"That's my story wrangler," replied Rosa. "It's what I use to pull stories down into my books."

Carly's face was awash with awe. "Can I touch it?" she whispered.

Rosa paused for a moment, considering, then said, "Has your mom ever told you about it?"

Carly shook her head, then nodded. "A little. She said you used something special to make your stories. She called it scary magic."

"Doesn't it frighten you?" she asked.

Carly shook her head.

"You can touch it if you'd like," said Rosa.

Carly walked up to the lasso and gingerly reached out with her index finger, lightly grazing the surface.

"How does it feel?" asked Rosa, her curiosity growing.

"It doesn't feel like anything I've ever touched before. It's not warm or cold. It's comfortable," she decided.

"It's like night air in summertime," said Rosa, smiling.

She walked over to it and pulled it from the hook. It pulsed to life at the contact of her hands as if it had a heartbeat; it matched the wild hammering of her own heart, beat for beat.

"Grandma, will you show me how to use it?"

"I could," said Rosa, hesitatingly, "but it'll have to be our little secret. You mustn't tell anyone, not even your mom."

Wide-eyed, Carly could hardly contain her excitement. "Why can't I tell anyone?" she asked.

Dialogues

How long must a poem be.
        words are eluding me
Months of instruction, yet
        I mouth soundless prayers
I'm still wracked with self-doubt.
        I need to lie down now
I ask "Do you like this?"
        feel grass stick to my back
Words; they are all just words …
        hear the heartbeat of ground
I hear *Nothing matters;*
        rock me back to myself
everything does. Listen—
        sunlight etches patterns
I've been asleep, deafened,
        inside of my eyelids
hear only one voice, one
        glyphs, runic talismans
no longer serving me.
        a crow caws *remember*
My pen finds the words, now.
        they fly on wind and wing

Pas de Deux

You reach
forward, poking
I curl
inward, clasping
a softly
molten middle.
Outside, I am
hardened
bristle
like prickly pear,
red
with fruit, overladen
potential
rotting on the trunk.
We circle
wary, brushing
barriers
unsoftened,
unbreached.
Like wind-pushed
bubbles, we
rise, merge in
iridescent collision
our margins
erased
to finally
—pop!

Christina Boschmann

Untitled

AN EXCERPT

Prelude

Full moon pulls tides
calls the chosen one
come home

darkest hour before dawn
eyes reflect
in mirror
one last time

hangs up phone
waves goodbye
walks to exit
let go and fly

sound of wings flapping
for the first time
silence   b r e a k i n g
in the valley

emerge 2016

flicker of a candle
momentarily lit
extinguished—
cold stone ground
      soak up blood.

Adagio

Dressed in black
polished leather
walk through mud
carry wreath
farewell message
printed on satin sheets

In unseren Herzen wirst du immer leben

vision blurred
through thick cushion of fog
salty rivers
run down face
      frozen red
leading the procession
to the hole
in which you will be put

white gloves clutching brass handles
shipyard rope
lowering box
into wet muddy soil
full of rocks

soul bombed
debris s c a t t e r e d
shockwaves ripple
halt—nothing to lean on

my legs tilt
clutching your shoes to my chest
my heart—ruptured
can't let go
not wanting to drop the white rose
into the gaping dark

Some flowers only bloom for one day

Lilies Tulips
dressed pure
in prime
floral sleepers
answered call for duty
        fresh cut humbleness
shining bright

Finale

rose bud ash
wilted flowers decompose

fingers trace
backwards
through the sand of time

emerge 2016

memories of children
travelling

heatwave
dry sun
waiting for the bus

to the lake
to the pool
cool down
on a dusty afternoon

your hand in mine

we run over green hills
disappear in horizon
trail of laughter
follow us behind

You trust me

dreamscapes

free-fall
looking up to heaven

Sunrise.
Giant orange ball ascending
over barren winter field

Look there he is going home

Juniper

Juniper Geranium
Juvenile Eagle Feather

Picture Frame
Crystal Rock

Feather
parting face in two

Dark   Light

Your black eyes looking at me
from the other side

Lion   Lamb

we exchange lamb for lion
I gave you a lion
you give me a lamb

Lion walks with you
Lamb huddles under my blanket

Candles dance

emerge 2016

Deliver the lamb with grin on face
we hug
I am short
You are tall

I am alive
You are dead

Quinn Anderson

General Arrangement

I remember that day—the way you laid the drawing paper down on the table, placed a lead duck on each of the four corners. You didn't look up and out the window towards Dundarave Beach which you always did, the water like a magnet for you, but by then the drawing or rather the seed of what was to become the drawing had taken you gently by the hand. Two mechanical pencils, the red one on the right side of the green, rulers and scales to the left, the overhead light positioned above for the days which would turn into nights as your imagination took you deeper and deeper into the lines. You brought your palms to the page, rested there for an instant as though reading braille and then pulled them in opposite directions over the surface from centre out to the edges. You did that a couple of times, smoothing out ripples on the Yangtze, taming imaginary waves on the ocean, caressing the page which would live and breathe you for months. I stood at a distance, amazed, wondering what kind of mind could pull a vessel together out of thin air—a vessel that would float 5,000 nautical miles from Nanjing to Vancouver.

Winter Garden

odd how a winter garden
can warn the heart

blossoms in sepia tone
burnt umber
stems
black, hollow
I always say summer

my favourite season
hikes along so many memories

of rivers, swims in mountain lakes
pungent smell of a seawall walk

but a stroll
any early morning
through a winter garden

with its frightening beauty
I'm on my knees

everything unkempt
gardeners gone awol

weeds striding out for an encore
mice having the run of the place

it's been too long
since I had my hands
in any kind of dirt.

Fortune Sticks

Was it at Doi Suthep in Chiang Mai
or the Royal Palace in Bangkok
where we threw sticks?

> *Life encounters difficulties*

in any case, I did it wrong
could tell from her huffing
No, like this, she said

> *like a splendid boat without rowers,*
> *beyond its power to go sailing*

flick of wrist
Muslim prayer
in a Buddhist temple

> *better moored on the coast*
> *than go along the wind*

the way she held her lips
as she tossed her pile
onto tile floor

> *however smart the boat,*
> *do not take a risk*

the stray one denoted fate
mine, I believe was questionable

> *should find expert for help,*
> *so boat can securely reach*
> *its destination*

Rattana sighed
put sticks back into cask
a sideways glance
then, looking down

likewise, in order to achieve goals
discussions with the expert
are suggested.

You'll try again tomorrow, she said.

Say a Prayer

3:21 a.m.   I slide
night guard into mouth
bite down, straight-jacket

on my teeth
to prevent idle thoughts
       telling tales

by the time I reach REM
La Catrina pays no mind
dentures, clickety-clacking
giving me advice

on the art of living
while cockroach crawls
deliberately   towards my door

lately, we're all dying
but when I was in Uruapan

I closed my eyes in the rain
found the skies open

willing to bestow on me
anything   I could imagine

kitchen cupboards locked up
the Senora's girl
gone home for the night

I dried myself off
went back to my room

near dawn   firecrackers
popping like gunfire

pockets emptied of pesos
ear-marked for rent, paella
in celebration of another Saint

Oh Virgin of Guadaloupe
tell me the point
of this late night rendez-vous
whisper wayward words
into my reluctant ear
caress my cheek
with your open cloak
invite my beating heart
to see what joy awaits us.

Emily Olsen

Christmas Baby

I'm sorry your birthday fell so close to Christmas.
Hot southern hemisphere humidity,
barely a breeze through the Kauri trees.

Sticky sheets, waiting.

No rules about sleep but we must stay in our beds,
"Read a book," Grandpa says, allowing a dim lamp.
My sisters are content with Nancy Drew and Trixie Belden
I suck on a nectarine pit—twirling my hair in another hand.

Sticky fingers, waiting.

The boys drift off before midnight,
reckless with their chance to stay up past bedtime.
I hear their slow slumber breath across the hall
fall unison with cicada's summer serenade.

Sticky insects, waiting.

The phone call finally comes and we jump from our beds in sleep—
drunk confusion.
Born in the wee hours, the last of six. The baby.
New-mother tired we talk instead to Dad whose tears come pouring
through the phone line.
"She's beautiful."

te amo

You were always so lovely to me; your third-wheel thumb-sucking freckle-faced little sister. The plain brown hair and knobbly knees in childhood photographs confuse my memory of your Cleopatra elegance, your slender olive-skinned legs. We shared a room; you, me and the scrape-scratch of eczema. Muted sounds of raw skin clawing. Back of knee bleed. I in deep-sleep bunk bed bliss. You, plagued with winter's wheezing asthma.

On the night of your brain surgery, seven ghosts appeared to me. I begged them not to take you. Sparing you, they returned instead, as migraines. They visited you often. They scared you and scarred you with painful reminders of mortality. You imagined another "end." You readied your doomsday plan, your "prepper" bag your earthquake kit. I bought you a compass and a knife thinking it would help.

"One day" comes: The survival-box food has expired. You're working in the soil now, taking photos of dragonflies and hummingbirds that visit your Eden. You're reading books and playing your old guitar again. We stroll through your garden with warm mugs of tea as the cool of dusk approaches. The bag full of beets you've proudly gifted me weighs a ton. I dare not pause to set it down, I don't want to interrupt your stories about the garlic crop, the sweetness of this year's carrots, the blueberry shrub debacle with the deer, and the night the wind took down the climbing bean lattice. You tell me all the genus names of everything you grow and occasionally bend down to pluck a weed, tending to your plants like children. Your hair parts at the back when you lean over and I see a flash of your scar, a reminder to me of your preciousness. A leaf is stuck to your sweater yet you barely notice as I gently brush it away.

The Weight of a St. Bernard

Small mercury engine puttering along the shoreline.
Hands, salt-stained, frozen to the steering wheel. Searching.
Small cove relief, imminent return to open water.
Odds, against us. Time, running out. Fuel, getting low.

The raven echoes our calls—not today raven.
"Shaman!" younger brother yelling, voice cracking.
Holding in my sobs—keep it together!
"Shaman!" I scream. Tears flow.

Exiled to an island for acting like a dog.
Wolf, St. Bernard, Malamute Cross.
Father gives a rare second chance.
Rescue mission.

A barking howl sounds from the point.
Canis Lupis reverberates across the water!
A massive plunge into the coastal cold,
a panting waterlogged brute swims toward us.

Wrestling the homecoming mass onto the boat
Skiff, capsize-near-miss.
Falling back into water,
whites of eyes enlarging with fear
panicking claws ripping my forearm.

Fall to the floor, hugging, friends; my brothers.
Tufts of sheep-shorn dog hair sticking to hands and faces.
Smell of family salvaged.

Grandma's Bunch

I'm not ready,
We still have the business with the family photos.
I want to sit amidst vodka slurred memory
and nod like I was there
I could pour you another and get the 7Up just right.

Now you smell like Old Lady Surrell's place
where I polished silverware for pocket money.

I peeked in the hall closet one time only.
You'd gone to see Judy for your hair appointment.
The ceramic Christmas place settings
were just out of reach on the top shelf.
I only wanted to look at them.

Where will your slippers go, in a box down in the basement?

On your sweater with embroidered roses you had an extra one added by
my name,
for the daughter I didn't know I'd have—Grandma's Bunch.

I pluck a single strand of hair from my head
and place it in the casket beside you.
I hold your hand, but
let go when I realise
there will be no more gin rummy.

Sylvia Symons

Hoferkamp Road

Mrs. Johnson wanted
fine-bone China
the Sunday her husband came knocking
at her teeth—a pink tea cup
rimmed with gold
to spit in.

The a.m. radio dance-along
　　　　stopped.
All three Johnson daughters
blanched into triage
became paper dolls,
thinly attendant.

The eldest led my elbow
to the dim living room
the drapes, the canvas lampshades
were heavy
while the daughters floated
like docile ghosts.

I stood by the picture window
I felt like a lake—cold on top
warm on bottom—a summer
inversion

a flipping of odds—teeth smashed
but fine-bone China surviving.

A mother's treasure

wrapped in crepe
from the day she lost her maiden name
to the blood-shot alkie
now crouched in the hall, eyes
bassett-hounding
down.

Rose? Rose? I'm sorry.

At dusk my mother ding-donged
the bottom entrance
to bring me home,
all three daughters
bare-foot on concrete
arranging their faces
in best Royal Albert smiles.

How was it? Mom asked
driving out of the gully
of Hoferkamp Road,
loose gravel rattling the bumper
a stub-tailed Doberman snapping
at headlights

I sewed a button on my lip

There was already talk
Those girls, not one of them look like their dad
But I knew the cool mornings
he made Swedish pancakes
with watered down molasses for syrup

his face thoughtful
waiting for batter to bubble
a glimmer of daughter in his eye.
He showed us his army tattoo, a blue inked
bird in the hand, two in the bush.

I sewed a button on my lip

and the Johnson girls nicknamed me Sliver
all summer we played outside in a rusty truck—front tires
sagging in a trickle of creek
before it ran
to the big Nechako,
pretended road trips on the locked steering wheel,
named our future babies
Serena Kate and Rachel Susan.

A regional park is down there now—
sporty families in mini-vans
with THULES on the roof.

emerge 2016

More sunlight in the gully
but all the names have been changed.
All three daughters gone,
registered under their
husbands. I can't find them now the road's
been paved—no trail of glass
no path
of broken teeth.

Hiding Behind Earl's Ride-on Mower

We squat in tall grass green—
       as tree frogs
and listen to the lady with the brown tooth
sing hallelujah.

       Dusk.

Not dusk enough for crickets,
dusk enough for dew—
cool beads on every
cross-hatched
blade of grass.

The lady sings
A better home awaiting
from her trailer at the bottom of Zwicky,
her voice carrying
moist
in a bucket we can't see.

We stay squat
on our haunches
cuz we learned about her church—
the strange
congregation

doesn't dance, they
dunk each other.
They twist their tongues
in gibberish then
lay down, slain in spirit.

We listen in a pasture
looking up at young-green stalks
each one will cut you
if you rub it
the wrong way.

Her song has hearse and undertaker
but most things here
are green and breathing—except
we three.

Our breath held in
as she sings.

Lisa Milne
Diner Series 1.1
AN EXCERPT

*A camel split open on the side of a bus, ribs winking through the
smooth strips of thick muscle, touting a limited engagement,
a chance to see the newest installment of Body Worlds.*

I saw the red-wire tangle of a rooster's circulatory system stand on its own,
cocksure, and I could think objectively of its dissection, the process of separating the meat to leave only an intricate nest of blood-vessels behind.

But the exposed tissue of those plasticized corpses, the human ones,
flayed open theatrically, their forms re-framed, refracted, reshaped, I
could only see them as caricature, *objets d'art* who gave their bodies for
witness of just one, single, cross-section of flesh, of action: the ice skating *pas de deux* in eternal extension, in exchange for some figment of life
after death.

It is the same. The repose. The embalming fluid. That intrusive duality
of sulphurous and peroxidic, a smell the exact opposite of skin, which you
try to ignore, not to breathe in, as you look at the face of your loved outside of a photograph for the last time, the very last time. Beautified with
the best intentions and care, but the mouth spread in too long a line, the
brow smoothed into a contour more similar to some other body part—a
shoulder perhaps—than a face. All while trying not to breathe the smell.

Imagine if she had not been reposed, but posed, rigged up with a
left foot and a right foot on each saddle, the spray of youth and balance
sweeping her hair back, forever engaged in that mythic act of riding two
horses at once.

Love Sick

You are very sick right now, throat in tatters, shredded and blistered and aching for three days. You are sweat-slick, soaking through sheets, two duvets, the front and back cushions of the New Red Couch.

From my half of the New Red Sponge, your giraffe-length limbs stretch over my lap. I watch you twitch in fever dreams. A neuronal hiccup in your cheek, where pallid skin pulls up thick covers of copper-wire beard, smooths the creases in your sleeping face, and tucks itself into the sputtered lullaby of bubbling breath.

I watch you sleep when you are well, too. I watch the micro-flutters of your eyelids, rapid movement beneath skin so thin the capillaries ripple over the rolling marble of your eye. You dream of finding me in a faceless other's arms. You dream of it and wake in the night, seek the weight of me beside you in the dark. You dream of it and wake in the morning, cold, until I tell you how I dream-sailed a dream-boat that dismembered itself into the waters beneath me. And then you tell me yours. And we fold into each other's arms.

I curl myself in the crook of you on the New Red Bed and the heat of your illness is an electric blanket, left on all night, the kind that burns old ladies in their sleep. The fault line between our bodies prickles, itchy and tight. Sweat trapped like condensation under glass—the low-pile shag of your chest hair, spill-soddened, the wheat fields of your legs, rained-out—until the dampness finds me and leaches into my fleece pyjama pants, makes them glisten like plaid morning grass.

I look at the long length of you, the angles of elbow and knee, at your curlicue hair barely constrained, the short sides I shaved at our kitchen table myself. I look at you and sensational phrases like heart-swell and caught-in-my-throat float to surface, a tanker-spill of love that chokes my highways and waterways with wanting only for the wisp of silver soul that lives in this lithe, bearded body to be content and happy, and healthy.

Sometimes, when you are falling asleep, not yet under, when you might still wake, I look at your face, just your face—not even counting the million things stuffed in your head, your heart—and a little grin creeps onto my face, unobserved, unselfconscious. If you opened your eyes you would see me grinning at you, inexplicably, which cracks me into a Vaseline-spread Beauty Queen, a Cheshire Cat, every deranged lover in history, until my smile rabbit-boils over and I laugh. You open your eyes. I tell you all this and you laugh, too.

Fish Food

We walk through a sea of scales, two-dimensional eyes, winking silver, a cloud waving in sequins where red twitches like a caught flame—red like nail polish, red like the Grand Am my mother won from Mary Kay—and catches my three-dimensional eyes among the fancier gradients of yellow-gold turning green-blue.

We squat at the glass to watch the fish move at eye-level, to be submerged in the small amazon tank and feel the presence of the pig-nosed turtle as he paws clawed leather flippers through the water, a train of prismatic worshipers behind him—a false idol perhaps, but a god among fish, the amphibious lord and master over the tiny bubble world they will all die in. We squat until our only young-ish knees ache, go numb, and crack-pop when we rise to stand.

I could, on tiptoe, dip my fingers into this curated river. Instead, I put my hand back into yours as we move into the tropical exhibit, unchanged in the twenty years since I came in a shimmering shrieking unblinking cloud of first graders, to see the piranhas.

I'd heard the horrors of the piranha tank, that it contained a repulsively pristine cow skull, evidence of the murderous talent and unrelenting hunger of the duly confined fish. I two spent weeks worrying about piranhas—piranha voracity, piranha mobility, piranha warfare tactics—fretting how only a six-year-old can fret, turning a thing over and over until the horror is more real than the bounds of their as-yet unchallenged life. Of course I would not witness the cow die, no, no, but I would be forced to look away from the tattered remains of a skull still fresh with flesh, strips of skin and muscle undulating in the water while the enormous spear-like teeth alternated dainty nibbling with snap-thrashing until the water frothed with tiny bubbles. I imagined piranhas fed exclusively on large live anatomies and, as I passed the tank, as they caught sight of my own tender young flesh, that they would smash their hard-boned fish faces against the glass, over and over, to break free of their domesticated safety, leap through shattered glass and fasten their hundreds of jaws onto my small limbs, sink into the plump of an arm muscle, chomp misguidedly on the thankless cartilage of an ear.

I came through the tropics with my school of open mouth guppies, walking practically backwards, peaking around the corners of my eyes, wouldn't even chance to look upon these horrors full-on. Rather, I would ease into view of the tank, slowly, minimizing my assured-panic so I might keep the calm-of-mind to fight them off, fling them off fast enough to escape maiming. And as the tank did slide into view and it became clear that their indistinct grey shapes weren't violently animated by the stink of fresh cow's blood, I turned slowly to look upon their un-holy forms.

Floating there, so docile, so humdrum, forehead- heavy but not enor-mous, efficiently-angled rows of sharp teeth, but tiny teeth (might as well have been toothless really) and their food so anemic, anesthetized, bloodless, boneless, that I was disappointed not to even have to be brave.

Today we peer at a handful of civil, institutionalized river monsters, their impulse to ruin dampened by so many years out of the hunt, only a pale shade of instinct left to distinguish carcass from deli-cut. A few bright bones are strewn across the tank's drab sand-bottom, to remind of the cow these aging predators stripped bare so many years ago (they could still do it, but now will not shed blood, nor tear).

These things come back to you because they never left, because you never left Vancouver and because they never could leave and I think home is always where the children are, as we leave my old foes to seek out the matted tangle of fur that is the two-toed sloth—the sloth never disappoints.

Fiction

Jackie L. Carmichael
The Catch

This excerpt is part of a novel in progress, "High Tide."

Seawater, everywhere, threatening father and son with its every wave, every drop. Fingers cramp, shaking as they grip the metal curve of the fishing craft's overturned hull that gleams oddly white against unending pewter sea. Brig Mulvey, over on the other side of the hull, encourages his son as he'd done for the past, what, eight hours? Thirty-eight years, in reality? A dogged cheerleader, right up to their present damn predicament. In the pickle of his life, Dad's still pretty damn cheerful, Greg thinks. Hell, he sang show tunes for a good hour. Tired of *The Sound of Music*. But it beat the Navy Hymn (the Nasal Hymn, he'd joked half-heartedly), morose with Brig's dolorous "for those in peril on the sea." Maudlin. "I'm here," Greg yells. Louder than he needs to. Cold, scared. Regressed to age twelve. Keely's washing up from dinner; she has no way of knowing he's late, that he's not powering into harbour, towards the lights of High Tide, but lurching like a barnacle on an untethered buoy, forty nautical miles from Dunmore East. Might as well be a thousand. No time to mayday, to grab a vest, send a flare. Certainly no time to cut loose that overloaded goddam net bag, to counter the torque of all that beautiful, disastrous fish. Salty tears roll in rivulets now, into his chapped lips. Parched. Damn thirsty. He ponders Keely, rounded, pretty in flannelette, the one with bunnies on it, his heavy woolen socks warming her toes. Fisher queen's lingerie, he called it. She'll slip into bed with a book, face shining, hair pulled back in a band. Prim. Lovely.

Another fishing boat'll come by. He must be alert so he can scream like a girl. They'll dive down, get the other two guys. Straining, he hopes for a clang from below. Phil and Rick made it, maybe. Trapped, pissed off, maybe. In a pocket of air, maybe. Cold. Mad as hell, but okay. Drink a beer on the way back to Dunmore East, laugh about it. Maybe. Where the hell's the self-inflating life raft with the "self-erecting canopy"? Who names these things, anyway? When they installed it on the deck, they'd guffawed about that "self-erecting canopy." Supposed to pop up if the boat went down. It did not. "Stay strong," he croaks, to himself as much as to Brig. The stories they've gone through, anything to distract from water, water everywhere. Vacations, relived. When Greg's kids, Zane and Chloe, were little. When Brig first came to County Waterford, when Brig met Peggy. Talked more than they had for years, desperate to keep the conversation going for what, eight hours? Hard to know, with his cell phone sitting like a little black electronic turd on the ocean floor. Unclench hands one at a time, spread throbbing fingers wide to keep blood circulating. Sun winks out, dipping below the horizon in a pocket of unsettling blood-red. Shifty-looking gulls circle like schoolyard toughs.

Greg plays it over in his head. No "weenie life jacket" for best buddy Rick, the more experienced of the two lifelong friends, when it came to fishing. The duo shoveled the netful into the hold, careful with the prime flesh. Then suddenly, slyly, the bounty shifted. Flipped the boat in a sort of fast slow motion, four seconds of rolling, silent horror.

Brig gabs a nervous streak, teeth chattering with shock again. Peggy, Sunday dinner, jukeboxes, the trip they planned to Canada. What's he going on about now? Lord, where the keys and repair manuals are? He thinks he's going to die. Greg flinches at the thought of a father-son deathbed talk. "Please stay strong, Dad." His voice is cracking. He's going to blubber, he can feel it. Breaking down won't help anyone. Stop it, he wills himself. What did Denise used to say? Look at a bright light, keeps a woman from crying when she needs to be professional. The sun is almost gone. Shivering resumes.

Brig doesn't have a life jacket.

"Dad, this life jacket is getting heavy. You wear it?" An evening star winks in, serene, unmoved by their predicament. The elder Mulvey, a stellar swimmer in his day, swam the Channel as a young man, but he's what, sixty-four? High blood pressure. Bum hip to boot. Greg should've talked him into quitting in spring; Peg begged him to, but it was "one last bumper season, just us boys on the briny ocean tossed." Twinge of guilt tightens his jaw. Life jacket itches where it touches his skin. Tired.

"Keep that damn vest on. So help me, I brought you into this world and—" Brig's County Meath brogue is faux-menacing in the night air.

"I know, you can take me out of it," Greg finishes, his heart turning over at the grim quip.

"Vest don't even fit," Brig says, serious now. He scrapes at something—Greg hears the *skitchy-skitch* on the hull. "Feckin' rust. Fisherman's work is never done." They want to cry; they laugh instead.

The *bloomp* like a deep sea fart, suppressed in the bowels of the overturned boat, resonates in the hull, in his core. "That can't be good," Greg says, his hand reaching across to grab Brig's callused paw. The sheer size of his father's hands has always astonished him. They can fashion a hook from a deer bone, whip up award-winning kettle at the fair, cradle a grandbaby, and fiddle a lullaby. All at the same time, Peg would brag.

"If we go over now, don't be grabbing at me," Brig blusters, teeth clenched tight against chattering. "You're on your own. I'll be saving my own behind, believe me I will. My portly figure's so padded, I float like the friggin' *Queen Mary*."

"I know what you're doing," Greg barks back, desperation welling where bile had been. Whining was never allowed. Not at the rink, benched when he wasn't fast enough or mean enough. Not when Peggy burned the schnitzel and the boys passed agonizing looks between them. "Eat that," his father would mouth at both of them, giving the two his best death glare. "It's delicious, Peg," he'd say, eyes round at the lie, and mean it.

"I love you, you rascal," Brig shouts as the boat upends. Father and son slide, then. Clumsy, flailing, without forethought. Into the waiting, cold, ungracious arms of that most pitiless of all mistresses, the Atlantic. "God that's cold," Brig gasps. Swimming's frenzied, with cold-stiffened limbs, spasmed fingers clawed from clinging to the hull. Get away from the *Pretty Peg*. Get away. A rush of roiling bubbles. Dead blue feet bob to the surface. Raggy jeans, then Pete's sandy hair, intertwined with seaweed and net against his sodden yellow hoodie, face down amid the traitorous silver of the day's catch. Greg and Brig reach out to the water-logged corpse with a single, sickened cry. Thwarted. The body's borne away on a wave, gone. Greg wails, then hushes, as he treads. His clothes are filled with water, but the water inside them is warmer than the water outside them. A mercy. "Dad!" he yells, then whimpers. Needing more mercy. Losing sight of the burly fisher who gave him olive green eyes and a stubborn streak.

"Here!" Brig crows, beaming. "Right with you!"

With that, a slip of a wave closes on the father, and on his raised, massive left hand, one huge thumb up. Then Brig's under. Loneliness is instant, awful. A stab in the gut. If he'd gotten Brig to wear the vest. If they hadn't cast that last net bag. If he had a boat to cling to. A best friend full of life. A father who wasn't drowned. A hope in hell. Now the cold is in earnest, and he spies it, twirling on a wave crest, maybe 100 yards away, or 100 miles, the life raft's little yellow shelter beckons. Well, look what's self-erecting. "Imagine your goal. Push on," Brig said when he taught the skinny twelve-year-old to swim punishing distances.

A smiling hologram of Keely seems to reach over the edge of the raft. Why hadn't he asked her to spend her life with him yet? His certainty no marriage could be as good as that of his parents? His rotten first marriage to Denise? That makes Greg think. The insurance policy is in the tin box under the bed. Will she find it? The raft flirts with him. Effin' tease. Closer! Water's cold, Holy Mother! I'm sorry I failed you. I promise I will do better.

Greg stills at the sight of a looming wall of water.

Rogue wave. It blocks out the raft and the evening star in a silent, vertical, inevitable rush. Greg wishes for a surfboard. Anything to cling to. He hears Brig's lilt. "Work with the sea." He holds his breath as the wave breaks. He opens his eyes, and through the dark salt water he sees a dull luminescence. The distant hold of the *Pretty Peg* drifts, slow, towards him and down, down. He tumbles in slow motion, no sense of bottom or surface now. He sees a dark figure, arms spread like the Saviour, and paddles towards it like a dog. Breath's running out. "Daaaad." The word escapes in bubbles like a string of pallid pearls from salt-caked lips. Like a prayer.

"Up here, boy!"

Greg lets his life vest do its work, then, up to merge with the voice, with the stars. *We move to what we love.* He coughs water, pulls air into his lungs. Not sight nor echo of his father. I'm hallucinating, Greg thinks as he heaves himself over the rounded edge with his last available spark of energy. Is he even on a raft? He feels the lull of sea under him. There would have been room for all of them.

He sees the flare gun in the flap.

Sonofabitch, he thinks.

Going home.

Loghan Paylor

Transubstantiation

Let's get one thing straight—this is not a love story. You don't believe me? We'll begin with our main character, Evan. He's just turned sixteen, he plays the clarinet, he has golden-blond hair and three zits on his chin. Got the idea? All right, roll cameras.

It is quiet in the basilica, and too early for the sunlight to reach the altar steps or to filter through the stained glass. Evan sits on a wooden pew, wishing he was back in bed. The church at this hour seems chaste and calm, the pagan liberties—candles, incense, wine—hidden away in vestibules. The pews slowly fill, as the organ warms to life with halting, laboured chords.

This trip is a gift to Evan from his parents, a reward for completing his confirmation back in May. They were originally going to give him a bike, but then his grandparents offered to take him with them on their pilgrimage to Basilique Sainte-Anne-de-Beaupré. Since Evan loves anything French—or international—but mostly because he wanted to see anything outside his hometown, he agreed to go, despite being the youngest person on the trip by at least forty years.

"Would you like to read?"

Evan turns and sees a young man standing at the end of the pew. Freeze-frame—this is important. He is dressed in the white robes of a cleric, high collared and loose sleeved. The man's eyelashes are thick and dark, fluttering like moth wings against nude eyelids. He is the youngest person in the room aside from Evan himself.

"Would you like to read?" the man repeats. This time Evan's grandparents overhear and cluck about what an honour this is and of course he would like to read, and Evan is dragged toward the front of the room, one grandparent on either side, behind the pulpit, and a Bible page is thrust in front of him. It is hard to read with his throat closing on every third word. The reading is forgettable, and later, when Evan scours these events in a search for narrative irony, for a coincidental clue, he won't recall a single word of it. When mass is over, he follows his grandparents meekly out of the church, avoiding eye contact with everyone.

This is the end of the prologue scene, and we're not coming back to it, so take note: Morning sunlight, now on the steps of the basilica, the priest extinguishing the candles and changing the hymn numbers for the next service. The young cleric is near the east alcove, replacing a dropped hymn book into its nook, but Evan doesn't see him. Freeze-frame and cut.

We shall skip ahead here, mercilessly, and avoid the tedious details of Evan's afternoon trip to Montmorency Falls, and how many pictures he takes, and the sunburn he will get on the back of his neck. In these days of instant technological gratification, no reader has the patience for scenic details or the careful development of dramatic tension.

Later that evening, Evan steps out of the corner store with a cherry-chocolate cone and a handful of change. The young man from morning mass is walking across the parking lot, white robes replaced by jeans and a blue turtleneck. Evan freezes, but the cleric catches his eye before he can look away.

"Hi," the man says.

"Hi," Evan mumbles.

"You're dripping."

"Excuse me?"

The man nods toward the ice cream cone, and Evan realizes he has dribbled cherry-chocolate onto his shorts. He tries to wipe the ice cream off without spilling his change or more ice cream onto the sidewalk.

Then the man offers to take the cone from his hand, and three napkins later, the coins are in Evan's pocket and the ice cream is once more under control, and somehow it is easier to exchange names and decide to walk to the park together.

His name is Paul. He is from Ontario, the southern part, but he left the farmlands as soon as he turned eighteen and went to Toronto to study theology. Paul plans to try for a clerical certificate in the fall. Evan asks about university, and Paul entertains him with stories of lecture halls and campus pubs and dorm life. He is twenty, after all, and seems to have a grasp on an adulthood which Evan longs for and cannot yet find.

It isn't until long after Evan's ice cream has disappeared and the remaining napkin has been rolled and twisted and shredded into oblivion that they realize how much time has passed. They walk back to the basilica together and say goodnight outside the seminary doors. Paul walks to his car and Evan goes inside.

They don't know yet, at least Evan doesn't. If Paul suspects, he doesn't say anything. There should be nothing in this scene to suggest otherwise, unless you want to read the ice cream as a metaphor, but that would be too obvious. Our boys are more innocent than that.

If there was a soundtrack for this story, it would be acoustic guitar, and maybe some traditional Québécois fiddle too. And don't eliminate the sun-glare on the camera lens. This light is omnipresent, remember, except in the park.

⌒

Evan's grandmother is delighted with Paul. As she eagerly tells her daughter on the phone a few days later, he is so polite, and intelligent, and so Canadian. Paul, to his credit, tries hard to live up to these compliments.

It is important that Evan's grandmother like Paul, for that is why she allows her grandson to go with him to Quebec City on the last night of their trip and to stay in his apartment for the night. A sixteen-year-old boy should not be allowed to wander the streets alone, and as a reliable young adult, Paul is entrusted with making sure Evan will not drink, he will not smoke, and he will not fraternize with girls.

Be sure to pick a good acoustic guitar solo for the travelling scene. Single shot out the passenger window. Focus on the details of the drive—the pink Frisbee left beside the highway, the price of coffee at the gas station, the license plate (1E5 2GW) on the car in front of them.

For our two boys, the downtown city is intoxicating, disorienting after the calm of the basilica grounds. Gone are the robes and the tourist shorts, replaced with T-shirts and jeans for both of them. Paul gets them into a bar, and they order beer and sit in a corner to watch the girls on the dance floor. The music should be new wave Francophone indie rock with plenty of electric guitar, and close-up camera work.

We will skip the dialogue, because it is hard to hear over the music, and it is a conversation that has been done many times. Evan is trying very hard to act like an adult, and Paul is trying to pretend he doesn't know what's happening.

A girl will ask Paul to dance. Evan will watch from the corner seat while they grind and sway under smoky, coloured lights. Paul isn't a good dancer, being more skinny than lithe and moving in awkward, jerky motions.

Evan finishes his beer and elbows his way across the dance floor to where Paul is grinding enthusiastically. The girl has draped her wrists across the nape of his neck.

"I'm tired. I want to go," Evan says, and squeezes his way through the crowd to the door, and then through the cloud of cigarette smoke surrounding the doorstep, out onto the street. He is halfway down the block before Paul catches up with him.

They don't speak on the drive to Paul's apartment, the silence deafening after the noise of the bar. Evan's stomach is churning uncomfortably from the beer and the way Paul's arm moves when he reaches to shift gears.

We will glance over their entrance into the tiny apartment, the second round of drinks, the midnight snack of oranges and crackers, the small talk that tries to cut the tension. We all know where this scene is going.

Paul is holding the last slice of orange. Evan is watching him. Paul reaches, and holds the orange to Evan's mouth. Close up on the contrast between the fruit and the pink of Evan's lips, the bead of orange juice that is just breaking through the pulp. It is like diving underwater, Evan thinks. It is like dropping into sleep—the half-second breath before the fall. Then that first kiss, as light as moths brushing wings in the dark. And the next. And the next. They don't talk much after that.

In our final scene, it is the next, and last, morning. Six a.m., the beginning of a day that will become scorching hot. The luggage is packed and loaded onto the bus that waits beside the road. The sky is a washed-out blue, and there are no clouds anywhere.

Evan hovers on the steps of the basilica, uncertain of many things, but at this moment unsure whether to follow his grandparents down the aisle, uncertain whether this mass, arranged especially for the departing pilgrims, will—ought to—include him. And there, caught in the morning light that threads through the stained glass, is Paul, dressed again in his robes. Red hands, purple head, white chest. He looks at him, and looks, and Evan makes the first of what will be many choices.

Then, in the east nave, while the priest recites the mass and Evan's grandparents stare heavenward, hymn books unfolded, voices singing the praises of Him, Evan and Paul are embracing, the folds of his robe covering them like wings, Paul's hand outstretched against the wall, pierced by one shaft of red sun, Evan opening his lips to receive that divine sacrament.

Jasmine Frances Sealy
Green Line

AN EXCERPT

Toronto smells unfamiliar to me at this hour, muddier somehow, like damp boots. I wait for him outside a Vietnamese bakery, and in the alley behind me two young hipsters dig through the trash, diving for their daily bread. I watch them until he appears around a bend, the foggy morning light obscuring his edges so that he seems not quite real until he is before me. We dither for a while, and his eyes avoid mine, settling somewhere by my chin.

"It's so early," he says by way of greeting.

I hate this. I hate everything about this. I was the one who insisted we maximize these final hours, but now, as we stand here, it is all too much. I feel his absence already, and it overpowers his presence like cheap cologne. We eat breakfast at Tim Hortons because he insists on experiencing every last drop of Canadiana before he leaves, and then we ride the green line to Scarborough. The Bluffs are as stark and lovely as I was told they would be, the cliff face reflecting on the lake in jagged triangles. Later, I will look at the photographs from this day and think the mirrored rocks look like the earth has been torn in two. But now I don't see this. I only see him.

We hold hands as we clamber across the beach because it feels necessary to be touching as much as possible. I say it is so typical of us to finally make it here just as we are about to break up and, when he laughs, I realize I was waiting for him to contradict me, but he doesn't. We walk back along Kingston Road where the sidewalks are littered with dog shit and trash. Once the greenery is behind us, there is nothing but chain grocery stores and nail salons to distract from the tedium of parting, from the practicality of ending.

Back downtown it is earlier than we thought it would be, and we don't know what to do so we head to the mall because at this point this couldn't feel any worse anyway. We drink coffee in the food court, and Eaton Centre is a carnival of humanity around us. He's rambling now about how great it is that the mall made the switch from disposable dishware because something-something-employment and the environment and a culture of disregard for the reusability of things something-something. Businessmen in cheap suits sit at the communal tables a few chairs down from homeless men and eat the same plastic fries. I watch them lick the salt off their fingers with the same vacant expressions and I say that all the world's a food court. When he nods in somber agreement I know for sure he has already checked out.

We walk west on Queen and as we pass the familiar wrought iron gates of Osgoode Hall I realize I hate this city. I always have. I hated Toronto from the first day I pushed an overloaded baggage cart through Pearson, scared, alone and unmistakably foreign. I hated snow after the first five minutes, trembling on the unshoveled sidewalks in my Keds because I didn't know any better. I hate my overpriced apartment. I hate the way people think where I live is scary even though most of my neighbours are yuppy gay guys who were just barely priced out of the Village. I hate streetcars. I hate street meat. I hate Caribana, an empty echo of Carnival back home. I hate the way these fourth-generation Jamaican boys say "zeen" and suck their teeth like they're fresh off a WestJet flight out of Kingston when they've never been further south than New York. This city has no identity. It absorbs the cultures of others, sopping up language and food and art and draining it back out, diluted and in poor taste. I hate this imitation city. As soon as I graduate I'll leave. I think maybe I could go with him. But then I remember that he never asked me to.

It seems as good a time as any to start drinking so we stop at the first patio with a free table and order a pitcher of something cheap. He's restless, running his fingers along the outside of the plastic jug as he watches people pass by. By my third pint I'm feeling grand. Resignation has enveloped me like a warm bath and I'm damn near content. I revel in alcohol-induced aplomb. I pull my hair up and off my shoulders so that he can see my neck and I make him laugh and I make him blush and for a moment I know I have a hold on him. Just for one moment I see him crack and I know this is not as easy for him as he thought it would be. I wield my power like an overconfident kid with a pellet gun. I switch to first person singular. I speak of grand summer plans with men whose names I make up on the spot. He probably sees right through it, but I'm too drunk to care. We order another pitcher.

I'm too loud and this was something he used to find endearing but now he glances around as if in search of an emergency exit. I ask him if he remembers that time we walked home in a snowstorm and I couldn't feel my face and he slapped me across it, not gently, and I laughed and screamed *again, again, again.* I ask him if he thinks American girls give good head. I ask him if he ever fucking gave a damn. When he gets up to go to the bathroom I think I've done it, finally, I've made it easier than ever for him to leave. But he comes back with a letter scribbled on a torn-up napkin. It says, *the line to the bathroom is really long.* I flip it over and write back, *i'm sorry.*

We pass notes back and forth across the table for a while. They say things like *nobody likes me. everybody hates me. i'm going to eat some worms* and *my hands smell weird and when we get home i'm going to fuck the shit out of you.*

remember when we met?

We shared a joint and watched the snow fall, shivering in our hoodies.

yes.

We stayed outside, long after the roach had burned to nothing. He told me he wanted to travel. He spoke of some ephemeral "more," though he never could explain what "more" meant to him. He said all he wanted was to make his world bigger.

i wanted to tattoo my number to your forehead. i wrote it on a napkin and you shoved it in your jeans pocket. i thought you would lose it.

He said the world is full of infinite experiences. Like grains of sand. And he just wanted to gather them up and build something worth living for.

i didn't.

And I knew exactly what he meant. I saw the sandcastle. I saw myself in the turrets, in the moats, in the sea glass windows.

don't go.

I think the problem was he saw me as the encroaching tide.

don't ask me not to.

I never wanted to make his world smaller.

ok. i'm sorry.

Eventually we run out of napkins so I am scribbling bad poetry on his hands and arms.

i hold him at the tip of my tongue like a word i once knew but have since forgotten. he is a train of thought, an idea that came to me in half-sleep but was gone before i woke.

He tells me to read it out loud and to pretend that we are dying. He says that anything can sound profound if we assume the author was dying when it was written. I read aloud from his wrist where I wrote *mine, mine, mine.* I pretend he is dying and I say it with gravitas, hand to my heart, my eyes locked to his. I say it over and over, more serious each time. Soon I'm crying and we're drunk so we leave the bar. We ignore the streetcar and stroll slowly down College. There are angry drunk men who gesture wildly from their motor chairs. There are punks, real ones like you don't see much anymore, eating pizza on Bay. There are real hippies too. Not like the hipsters who strut on Kensington in their Aztec prints and fake moccasins—real leather-skinned, matted-hair hippies with dirty feet and nails and clothes. We walk past the preppy blond boys with their pretty Asian girlfriends and the queens and the Filipino boys blaring dance-hall music outside Bathurst Station and our feet keep hitting the pavement as we head west and all of Toronto smokes and laughs and sings and screams and dances and curses and sweats and breathes around us.

No one falls in love properly anymore. So we get high in a back alley and make sloppy love against a garbage skip. I don't know how we make it home but we do and there we fuck again. The next day we don't wake up until noon and the light streams in through the curtains and the sun shines yellow on the financial district where good men and women work nine to five. I don't know how I will survive this city without him.

We make breakfast, the egg yolk dripping down between our fingers and congealing on unwashed plates. Then I walk him down to the bus stop. The school kids are coming home and all the Filipinas and Sri Lankans are playing with little blond babies in the park and I wonder who takes care of their babies all day while they mind those who belong to the good men and women who work in the financial district. I want to ask him this, to engage him in a debate on white feminism and critical development theory and epistemic advantage and whatever else I can think of to buy myself ten more minutes. Instead, I kiss him one last time and hold him tightly around his wrist where my desperate plea has smudged illegible, then I let him go.

Emmet Matheson

Saddle in the Rain

AN EXCERPT

Our investigator, Aesop, is beaten up by thugs who believe him to be Hislop, the previous tenant of Aesop's office. Usually lethargic, Aesop takes initiative and tracks down Hislop's old receptionist with the help of his officemate, Roz.

Aesop Mosley rode the elevator up sixteen floors over West Broadway. He couldn't remember the last time he'd travelled so fast by this means. Sixteen floors on West Broadway went a lot faster than three floors in an East Hastings SRO elevator.

Aesop squinted at the abstract reflection of his battered and stitched face in the sleek, polished elevator doors. In quiet moments like this he could feel the swelling throb, and the pain felt sharper.

Judy, Roz's Facebook friend, had apparently moved up in the receptionist world. Aesop was familiar with the dank East Van pulchritude of Judy's former workplace. The front entrance to the Westside fertility clinic, by contrast, was sterile. No plants even. Soft rock from somewhere in the ceiling panels, like Wilson Phillips lived upstairs.

If Judy had advanced her station, her wardrobe had yet to catch up. She was dressed in that haphazard mix of punk, goth, and rockabilly styles popular among roller derby revivalists. It seemed like a put-on to Aesop, but then, he paid rent on an office with the words Private Investigator on the door. Who was he to judge other people's games of daytime dress-up?

"You're the guy Roz told me about, right?" Judy said.

"Yeah, how'd you make me?"

"You don't look like the kinda guy who stays up all night worrying about his sperm count."

"So, uh, how long have you worked here?"

"Since Cousin Phil closed his warehouse."

"Phil Hislop is your cousin?"

"No, everyone just calls him Cousin Phil. I don't know why. He must be cousins with someone who matters. He'd been Cousin Phil for a long time before I met him."

"Do you know where I could find him?"

"Who, the cousin?"

"No, Hislop. I'm looking for Hislop."

"You don't wanna find Cousin Phil. He's a creep."

"How long did you work for him?"

"Five years, on and off."

"On and off?"

"Yeah, sometimes he'd shut down the office for a few months at a time when he'd go away on business."

"And what, exactly, was his business?"

"Oh, you know, import/export."

"What does that actually mean?"

"He bought and sold stolen goods. Sometimes drugs."

"Ah, okay, thanks for that. Can you think of anyone who'd want to hurt Hislop?"

"Hurt like how?"

Aesop waved a hand over his bruised and stitched-up face.

"That's what this is about?"

"Honestly? I don't know."

"Shit, son, I had my face busted up worse than that at derby lots. Just in practice once."

Roller derby. Bingo.

"You oughtta learn how to protect your face. It's hard to tell with all the swelling, but you just might be a looker. Come closer. You lose any teeth?"

"Not since I was twelve."

"Cute mouth, anyway. You say Cousin Phil did this to you?"

"Not exactly."

"I didn't think so, that's not his style. He's more of a kneecap kind of guy."

"What do you mean?"

"I mean he doesn't hit people in the face. I don't know. Maybe it's, like, too personal. He likes to smash people in the knees with a hammer."

"A hammer?"

"Yeah, he kept it in a drawer in his desk. Every now and then he'd hit someone in the knee with it. You gotta understand, the people he did business with…. It's a, uh, a sales tactic, right? Let me tell you, that shit would not fly here. But we scar people all the same. Believe me."

"So, listen, you know where I could find him? Hislop? Cousin Phil?"

"I don't know. I figured he was leaving the country when he closed the office. But it's been a while, right? He wouldn't stay away forever. He likes the coffee here."

"You know where he gets his coffee?"

"One of those Commercial Drive spots. You know, a real Italian place."

"You know the name?"

"I'd know it to see it. You got a car?"

⌒

"Fuck the Number 20," Judy said at the Broadway SkyTrain Station, so she and Aesop took Commercial Drive on foot. The midday sun was bright behind them but there was a cool wind from the north. Aesop was looking forward to the inevitable coffee he'd enjoy once they arrived at whichever coffee shop Judy recognized as Hislop's.

They passed the coffee shop where a cross-cultural contingent of smokers had taken a final stand against encroaching health bylaws and displaced Yaletowners, the coffee shop favoured by frustrated screenwriters and male models once linked with Paris Hilton, the coffee shop where Aesop once rescued a dog that didn't actually need rescuing, the Starbucks that seemed likely to get targeted by anarchists but didn't, the coffee shop where there was never anyone behind the counter, the coffee shop where the other coffee shop's only employee always was, the coffee shop where there'd once been a shooting during a televised soccer match and when the police showed up the victim was the only one still there. There was the coffee shop favoured by players of the didgeridoo and djembe, the coffee shop favoured by the dope dealers (also the coffee shop favoured by the police), the coffee shop favoured by inscrutable old men with impossible moustaches and walking sticks, and finally, the coffee shop whose staff lived up to every mean-spirited stereotype about elitist hipsters. Even bitter and cynical Aesop admired the craftsmanship of the hipster joint's coffees and baked goods.

Aesop said as much to Judy after their thirty-five-minute walk from Broadway to Venables.

"I don't know," Judy said, looking south at how far they'd come. "They all kind of looked the same. I think I need another look."

"I need a goddamn coffee," Aesop said, and walked into the hipster enclave without bothering to check if Judy was following him.

"Hey," said the skinny barista behind the counter. He wore a curled moustache and braces over a tie-dyed Miley Cyrus t-shirt. He pointed at a chalk-covered sandwich board near the door that read NO DERBY CHICKS and shrugged. "I don't make the rules."

Aesop looked back at Judy, who looked at Aesop and then at the barista and then at the sign.

"The fuck?!"

She was over the counter and had the barista up by his braces and slammed against the wall before Aesop had even processed the fact that he would not be getting his long-awaited Americano here.

"Aw, hell," Aesop said.

Judy issued a steaming stream of profanity into the barista's face.

Aesop couldn't tell if the barista was crying or if that was just Judy's saliva running down his face.

Aesop opened the covered jar of biscotti on the counter and helped himself to something with nuts and a chocolate covering. Now the day hadn't been a total waste.

Aesop walked outside alone, turned the corner at Venables and got an Americano at the coffee shop inside a movie prop warehouse. The Americano was okay but the barista was cheerful. Aesop walked out into the gray sunshine with his hot drink and watched the chaos in the hipster cafe from a safe distance across the street.

Eventually Judy got bored or merely ran out of things to smash and walked out. Aesop waved and she jaywalked over to him.

"Where'd you get that?" She jutted her chin at his coffee. "What about me? I don't get a coffee?"

"You like biscotti?"

"Thanks."

"That wasn't the place, was it?"

"What place?"

"Hislop? Cousin Phil? That's not where he liked to get his coffee, is it?"

"Fuck if I know. I just wanted to get out of the office and beat someone up, you know? You ever wanna do this again, you know where to find me, right?"

Judy broke the biscotti in half with her teeth, put half in Aesop's lidless to-go cup, and kissed him on the cheek. Aesop stood there, on the corner, watching her walk back down towards Broadway as the biscotti disintegrated in his Americano.

Coranne Creswell

The Trophy

**AN EXCERPT FROM THE NOVEL
"WHITE BONES, GREEN GRASS"**

Lewis and Ray were twins sharing one father. There was only one .22 calibre to inherit, so a second one was purchased. The boy who selected the longest match from the fist of their sister June got first pick. Lewis got lucky.

"I'll take Grandad's." He liked that it had been held in the young hands of his old grandfather and then passed on to his own father, and that its history included the Christmas goose and other meals their family had gathered around. Ray wanted the new one anyways. He expected it to be more accurate and to have a better design.

They were going for grouse, an abundant bird that is tender and delicious fried in butter. Already familiar with snaring and eating them, Lewis read in his *Stokes* bird guide what he didn't already know. He knew that they ate catkins and seeds, that they nested on the ground, that they had feathers in their nostrils and that the scales on their feet helped them walk in snow. He could tell at a glance the difference between a spruce and a blue, a male and a female. He was armed with his hand-me-down rifle and an ornithologist's head of facts.

They rode into the backcountry with their dad on the ATV. Uncle Jack and their least favorite cousin, Reno, followed on a second one. Reno was a few years older and, by his own estimation, better at everything.

It was still dark and they had guns. Lewis and Ray were schooled by a father who emphasized safety and a cool head. There were enough stories of tragic firearm accidents due to a careless attitude, the injury done to and by a family member or close friend. They were quiet and careful not to give a reason for anyone to doubt their pending maturity, though any other day would find them leaving garter snakes or mice in each other's boots or hiding the other's hockey stick until the last minute before leaving for practice.

The mellow light of morning sluiced through the trees reaching for them as they edged, now on foot, along the trail. Reno, who had elected his own self to lead the way, put a hand up to silence the others, though they hadn't yet made a sound. The first grouse stepped out, oblivious. Reno called it and took the easy shot.

"Chicks just can't resist me, eh?" he said.

Lewis ignored him and Ray rolled his eyes.

Later, they heard the wing beats, soft like the fast fluttering pages of a book. Lewis planted his feet and pulled the stock of his Winchester .22 calibre to the curve of his shoulder. He pulled the trigger just as the bird cleared the bush. The grouse dropped in a puff of feathers.

Ray had stepped back to relieve himself when the next bird flushed. Lewis got that one in the air.

"Way to go, bro," said Ray, happy that it hadn't gone to Reno, but his mood shifted. Adolescent boys are wired for competition. The score was Lewis 2, Reno 1, and Ray 0. Ray was a crack shot. At home, when Lewis would throw a pop can weighted with gravel in the air, his brother would get it three out of four times.

Perched on rocks and logs, they ate May-Bee's cookies and drank sweet coffee in metal cups. Amos and Jack rolled Drum tobacco cigarettes, remembering out loud the lore of firsts: first gun, first buck. They recalled the biggest elk they had ever seen and the time they had gotten in between the mother and cub and how lucky they were to be sitting telling of it. Hunting with his boys was a new first for Amos.

Lewis leaned back to watch the ravens in the branches above them. He was paying attention to what most people don't bother with. He noticed the way their blue-black feathers folded in perfect order down their bodies. He listened to their throaty vocalizing, the sound both soft and sandy, chortling, cocking their heads side to side as if discussing the strange ways of the two-legged species. They were undoubtedly aware of the cache of grouse—smartest opportunists around.

"I'm saving up to get my first buck's head stuffed and mounted," said Reno. He was fixated on trophy hunting. At school his older crowd stood in circles smoking cigarettes, their hands plunged deep into pockets, turning slightly to spit masculine gobs of phlegm behind them. They would discuss contenders for the Stanley Cup, the kind of pickup truck they would like, and the number of points that were on a buck that got away. Also the developing breasts of girls they had known their whole lives. Trophies came with sticks and pucks, on wheels, and four or two legs.

"Why don't you and Lewis come back out just before sunset when they'll be moving around again?" Amos said to the son who was anxious to keep looking.

Lewis was familiar with the side of Ray that would be moody until he got a goal or a home run. In a need to individuate, twins sometimes try to outdo each other, but Lewis never went that route. Their twinship was like being counterweights on a scale.

Gravel rained that afternoon as Ray restlessly honed his skills blasting cans that Lewis tossed.

Amos told them: "When you find one, immediately walk in on them and take your shot. If you flush a bird but fail to down it, don't hesitate to follow. Just start looking up instead of down, because chances are that bird will settle in a tree."

They walked between the gravel road and the forest edge towards the finish line, a waning pink horizon in the west, stopping to listen for scratching in the dirt or the shuffle of a grouse dusting itself. Lewis and Ray weren't the only hunters. They spotted the silent owl in a nest built in a tangle of witch's broom high in a northern white spruce tree. A soft-throated purr came from the undergrowth. Lewis leaned in to see the camouflaged grouse plucking through the dense bush.

"I think it's a hen," Lewis whispered.

They got down on their bellies eye-level with the mother, who cooed and clucked to her bevy of chicks a few metres away.

"Oh shit, she's got babies. What do I do?" asked his brother.

They were outdone. Neither was going to make a move, so together, like they had done their entire lives—eating most of their meals, roughhousing on the floor, and sleeping in parallel twin beds—they watched, suspended in a sweet moment of an ebbing childhood. Ray joked that his great day of hunting was outdone by balls of fluff on legs. They laughed at what tough guys they were.

"You know that saying? 'Get the bear before the bear gets you'?" Ray said.

Designed for stealth more than any other raptor, the owl flew on breathless wings. In the briefest of moments, with a tilt of its flight feathers, it dropped like a phantom. Talons closed, panic followed, small feathered bodies pressed their breasts to the earth, and their mother was gone. Lewis was in awe. Ray was angry. His reflex, lightning fast. With one eye closed he squinted down the barrel to where the great horned owl flew. He fired, his aim accurate. Lacking all his usual grace, the great hunter fell. *Thump*. His final landing, his wings barely retracted.

Lewis cried, "Noooo!" He snatched the gun from Ray's hands, threw it in the dirt and ran towards the owl.

Adrenaline rising, boys running. It was still alive, opening eyes halfway and closing them, blinking slowly. The grouse was still alive too, but labouring without fight, still clenched by a sharp talon that had pierced its tender neck.

"You have to kill it." Lewis said. He couldn't look at his brother.

Ray, who had recovered the gun that he had polished that afternoon, put a lethal bullet in the big raptor.

Lewis pulled the hen from the now relaxed talons, granting it relief by a swift twist of its neck until the vertebrae made a soft pop. He took his rifle in one hand and the limp body in the other and walked away from Ray and the dead owl.

"Lewis, we could get it stuffed," Ray called after him, plaintive. "To honour it," as if it was a higher calling to be a stuffed animal than a living, breathing one. "It's a trophy," he said, trying to muster some bravado reminiscent of Reno that would bury some other feeling he couldn't look at.

Lewis turned, walked straight to his brother, with whom he had spent nine months in simultaneous gestation, curled like commas in the same womb. He grabbed his shirt, pulling Ray's face close to his own.

"There is no such thing as a trophy. There is another owl out there sitting on a nest waiting for him to bring food for babies that will be easy pickings for a raven or hawk if left alone. Did you know that owls mate for life? There is no such thing as a trophy." One heavy step closer to being a man, he walked alone back to the farm.

Ray came home with the strap of his .22 across his young, lean, and bare twelve-year-old chest. He carried the orphaned chicks bundled in his own shirt. After placing them in a cardboard box, he constructed a pen out of chicken wire. He fed them grain and kitchen scraps for another month before releasing them, until they were past the age when they would be leaving their own mother. Sometimes when he did things around the yard he let them out, while keeping an eye on the farm cat. They followed him everywhere, climbing on his shoulders to roost if he sat still long enough. It was the best he could do.

Sandi Myrlene
Frozen in Time

An excerpt from the novel "Frozen in Time." Samantha, a forensic pathologist, meets Brandon, an RCMP officer. The next day, she has a panic attack when he suggests they fly in a helicopter to the site of a body encased in ice. The following scenes occur after Samantha recovers.

Samantha:

After having a wonderful supper, I finally look at Brandon and sigh.

He smiles tentatively. "I could go out to the scene, do the work, and retrieve the body, then when I get back you can do your autopsy. Okay?"

"I can't let you do that. Besides, if I don't go to the site, I'll feel like something might have been missed. No reflection on you, please don't think that. It's just my method. From beginning to ending, I need to be there."

"So," Brandon gestures, "how do we get you there? I mean, I know fears. Fuck, I'm afraid of getting shot in my junk." He turns beet red and looks down, coughs, and then, looking up he continues: "I am also afraid of having to kill someone in the line of duty. I mean I would do it, I just can't conceptualize the need for a person's death." He shrugs.

I smile at him. He has a conscience. Wow, what a great quality. "So, I am guessing that you have never had to kill someone?"

"No," he says, "I've been lucky so far. I've had to maim but I haven't had to kill." He crosses over his heart like a Catholic person would. Then he smiles and laughs, "I'm not even Catholic. Have you ever flown in a helicopter?"

I shudder visibly, "Yes and no." He looks perplexed.

I continue: "I saw Niagara Falls when I was six months old. And when I turned twenty-five, I decided that I wanted to see the falls again because even though my parents have pictures of me at the falls, I honestly don't remember being there at six months." I smile.

"That makes sense," Brandon says, but looks confused.

"So at twenty-five, I decided to go again. I flew to Hamilton, and then rented a car and drove to Niagara Falls. I decided I wanted to get the best view I could so I took a helicopter ride over the falls. I love taking pictures, so I knew I could get some great shots. I was excited. And a little scared. I am petrified of heights. When I drive over a bridge, I look straight ahead; I can't stand on a ladder and change a lightbulb. My uncle took me to the CN Tower and when I realized that the elevator was glass, I copped out. I even jokingly told him that I would climb the stairs to the top, but couldn't take the elevator. I can go on, but I think you get my drift.

"Anyhow, after paying my $100 for the ride, I had a half hour to wait. I took an anti-anxiety pill to reduce my nervousness. But waiting and stewing, my anxiety ratcheted up until I was sure I was going to pass out. Finally, it was time to get in the helicopter. I did, and I sat down.

"The pilot told us about the trip and stated that he would let us know when it was a good time for pictures. Everyone fastened their seatbelts, and we took off. As the helicopter lifted, it swung around in an awkward motion. I wanted to throw up. I thought I was maintaining control well. I didn't want to ruin the trip for the others. One of the passengers looked over at me smiling, but quickly the expression on her face turned to worry. She asked me if I needed her to get the pilot's attention and I nodded yes. I guess I wasn't hiding very well after all. I like to think I would have been okay once the helicopter smoothed out, but I will never know. The pilot returned to the platform and I was assisted out." I laughed. "I even remember the idiot that tried to sell me a picture of myself getting in the helicopter after I returned. What an idiot! Did he honestly believe I wanted a souvenir?" I shook my head and shrugged.

The waitress comes over to ask if we need anything else. We both nod. Smiling at me, he asks, "Do you think you can do this? The flight will take about thirty-five minutes. I'm worried for you."

"Thank you," I smile, reaching over and squeezing his hand.

He squeezes my hand back. Then we sit in silence until the waitress arrives with our drinks.

After taking a long sip, I lean back in my chair and sigh. "I want to do this. But I'm going to need your help, Brandon. Do you think you can help me?"

"Of course." He looks genuine. "I'll do whatever you need me to do."

So I tell him what I need from him, and he appears to have no issue with it.

⸙

Brandon:

I pick up Samantha at the hotel around 10:15 a.m. We head to the airfield, and I hold onto her hand as she requested the day before. I will hold her hand through this entire ordeal. I have to give her credit: she is shaking hard, but she tells me that she has taken her medication and, in my truck, she focuses on deep breathing. Inhale, count to ten, exhale, count to ten, and so on. I asked her when I picked her up if music would help, so Aerosmith is playing. She really likes the band too. Cool, eh!

I am not to talk to her while we drive, as she wants to focus on her breathing and listen to the song, "Janie's Got a Gun." As she listens, she starts to sing along with the music. Samantha has a beautiful voice. One more thing to instantly like about this woman.

The sun has been up one hour when we arrive at the helipad. I park the truck and run around to the passenger's door. As I take Samantha by the hand, she squeezes mine tightly, her nails digging in. I hiss slightly. I can see that she is starting to tear up. I whisper into her ear that she should look at the sky. She looks up and a low gasp comes from her mouth. "It's beautiful," she whispers to me.

Drawing her into me, I drape my arm around her shoulders with my one hand still holding hers. Cuddling her, I walk us to the pad, help her into the whirlybird and follow after her. We put our seatbelts on. As soon as she is finished with hers, Samantha grabs my hand and I squeeze hers tightly. I introduce her to Tom Manner, our pilot. He smiles and greets her. I informed him earlier of her fear, so he knows not to ask her anything. He lets us know he will be taking off now, and tells us to put our headphones on. This is so we can all hear each other. As soon as we do this, I start asking her questions, making sure that she is continually looking in my eyes. I hold both her hands in mine. So I start by asking her about her job. "How long did it take you to become a forensic pathologist, Samantha?" She told me that it would be important to state her name over and over again and maintain eye contact while asking questions.

"Fifteen years," she says while looking into my eyes.

What? I think to myself. That's a fucking long time. I collect my thoughts. "What does that entail?"

"Four years undergraduate, four years medical school, four years residency, one year fellowship, and four to five years certification, or fifty autopsies—whichever comes first. I did fifty autopsies in two years. I studied at the University of Tennessee's Anthropological Research Facility. It was a fantastic experience studying human decomposition in a variety of settings." Her eyes twinkle.

"Wow, that's a lot of schooling Samantha. You must have been incredibly motivated."

"I was. I've wanted to work in this field for as long as I can remember."

As I look directly into her beautiful deep brown eyes, I ask her about her time at the University of Tennessee.

"It was the most exciting time of my career," she pauses. "Of my life! Although most people have no idea what I'm talking about when I talk about the Anthropological Research Facility, most have heard of 'the body farm.' As an RCMP officer, I figure you would have heard of it."

As she smiles mischievously at me I grin, "Yes, Samantha. I have heard of it, but I've never been there. A lot of the knowledge I have on body decomposition comes from readings of the goings-on there." Laughing hard, I continue, "As an RCMP, I definitely knew what you were talking about."

"So basically what happens at the 'body farm' is that people donate their corpses. Upon the bodies arriving at the University of Tennessee, they are autopsied. According to the focuses of decomposition cases, each body is placed in a certain situations … buried, unburied, underwater, or in the trunk of a car. It also provides region-specific data. Then each body is autopsied again to view what has happened to it after it has been in the field for a determined amount of time, under specific conditions. At the body farm, we can figure out the what, when, and how. The information obtained is crucial to police work."

Samantha:
"Samantha," Brandon nudges my arm, stating excitedly, "We have landed, you did it!"

"I did it. Thank you." I smile while I squeeze his hands before letting go.

H.C. Phillips
Object,—Obsess,— Compulse,—

The asphalt is too dirty. He doesn't want to look down at it but he has to watch his feet. There, atop puddles of murky water, the steely sunlight struggles and wanes. Car headlights flash as they pass; he squints and cringes away. Oily patches on the road reflect a spectrum of browns to dark violets—unwelcoming colours that wash slowly down tar grooves and cracks to gutters.

Nothing remains in the angry void left in his hopes' wake. Nothing but for the slow, steady pelt of the icy rain. He focuses on the rhythmically falling droplets until they calm him, and he can slow finally to a stop. He looks to the sky, seeking relief. It provides him with substitutes much more satisfyingly cool and pure than the salty, warm streams that are confined to the repeated path from the corner of his eye to the side of his jaw.

Excitement runs to his fingertips, electric as though his touch could breed brilliant white light. Compared to the racing of his heartbeat and tumultuous thoughts, the figures in gowns and suits move too slowly.

He is braced, ready. He is waiting for the time to come when he will leap all the way to the altar from the cold, hard pew. He smiles because he knows—he knows—this is the right thing to do.

He walks, a solitary figure in military grey trench coat reaching down to knees and damp shins. He walks, in sodden shoes, discomfort displaced so long as every breath is even and counted in sets of three.

Desperate, smothering fingers of cold invade through his old tattered coat and the suit beneath; sink deeper, deeper than his skin, into his mind and his thoughts until thinking itself is sharp icicles pounding his skull. It is always, must always be, this same coat, same shoes, same tweed hat, same black dress suit, even if they are aged and scuffed and worn off-colour, hanging slack and loose on his gaunt frame.

The rain hardens on his face. He senses some turmoil in himself, but he does not understand it. He lets his head drop back down and sound pounds around his ears on the stiff brim of his hat. He can hear some distant chant in his mind, that this time is the last, but he is not sure how long he has been chanting it. He removes his hat to quiet the pounding. Droplets quiver at its rim. He detects some lingering impression throbbing at the base of his skull that he is sure is important, is the source of everything, is the only thing that matters. Resolution stirs in him, as though on the edge of knowledge, and some sense of shame and regret fades away.

He stands up. He is not ashamed. He will let everyone here see his face, know his heart, even if the force of their gaze burns at his skin. It is what he didn't do and so what he must do now, to make it right. This time, it is his last chance. He will not hesitate.

His heart is tight with the pressure of unspoken words, their meaning waiting to be realized, to be heard, to be understood. Words that he must rely on when language so often fails him. Inadequate. Yet it is all he can use and so he must offer his words. He has dutifully awaited the appointed time in the ceremony and will not—cannot—wait any longer.

❦

He is focusing only on retracing his steps, the exact steps, as exact as they can be, moving his legs quickly but taking short, agitated strides often broken awkwardly to avoid large puddles and seams and cracks in the pavement that threaten to unhinge him. Every accidental splash is deeply unsettling and so he must focus on the steps themselves and where they lead to hold his nerve.

❦

A car veers unexpectedly, too fast, out from around a corner, a black Cadillac bedecked in white wedding tape, and for a moment he thinks it will surely lose its grip and hurtle into him. He cowers and shrinks away, clumsily replacing the hat on his head, a new wave of self-conscious shame and regret washing over him, and to disperse it he walks on, unhappy energy powering his forceful movements.

❦

The veiled face is not right. He rubs at the heat burning up from beneath his collar, uncomprehending. The energy from moments before, deflecting inwards. All around him, their eyes, watching. He cannot look at their wrong faces. Rubbing harder. His eyes, flickering this way, that way; away. Failing to make eye contact. To connect. There is nowhere for him to turn, so he drifts away from them—he stands, his joints simply locked into place, but is outside this reality, in another time.

They whisper and he hears them and knows that he has failed to explain. They have rejected his words, and have rejected him. He is sure that if only he could have expressed it better, they would surely all understand. If they could just accept him, it would make this right at last. But he is already tumbling away from himself, closing himself away from them.

❦

A shop door left ajar is quickly shut as his passing displaces cold air into unwanted places, sealing him off with only the empty streets for company. The smell of food and warmth lingers and he jerks his head involuntarily away. There is nothing but his own deep need feeding his hollow stomach.

And the need is engorging, expanding; he is getting closer. He hesitates only briefly before crossing the street, unwilling to lose his momentum, swinging arms restlessly as he glances for traffic, noticing peripherally the cold, wet, empty miserable grey of his surroundings only in that it shouldn't be like this, and he clicks his tongue three times to try to dislodge the feeling that it isn't right.

☞

The church bells toll.

It is near, since he can hear it over the rain and past the buildings of the winding streets. He feels a familiar urgency, a compulsion, surfacing. All of the wrongness about the day falls away because he will soon be able to rectify this one key wrong of his past.

There is nothing else in this moment, just an eager swell of deep emotion, waiting to be released. He stretches out with difficulty to span the threatening puddles, but now he is smiling broadly—knowing, knowing that this time it is the right thing.

☞

His collar is upturned, his hands deep in his pockets, and though he walks on he may as well be unmoving, for the background of brick buildings continues monotonously against a skyline of church steeples and factory chimneys.

Martina Wolff
Retail Kings

AN EXCERPT

"Excuse me."

Nope.

"Excuse me, young man."

If I'm not looking at you, I can't hear you!

A firm tug on my shirt sleeve. "I said, excuse me, young man!"

Finally looking up, I put on my most dazzling smile, which was hard, because as soon as I saw who was being so disgustingly persistent, I wanted to rip off my ears.

Refolding is about the most tiresome, repetitive task a retail clerk will have to do. If Sisyphus were alive today, I'm pretty sure he would have to refold endless rows of t-shirts instead of rolling a stone up a hill. The thing is, even if you manage to refold a whole table of clothes and not get interrupted, the moment you turn away there's bound to be a customer who walks up to precisely that table and starts ruffling through your freshly folded masterpiece. And by ruffling I mean turning it into a thrift store bin within seconds. So what it comes down to is, you find yourself refolding the same fucking t-shirt over and over and over again. Even Mother Teresa would freak out at some point.

Bearing this in mind, I had found a way to minimize the misery of this task. I always stood right in the aisle, in front of the table, head down, eyes fixed on the item of clothing I was working on. This way I not only blocked any customers from coming near my table, I also could pretend that I didn't notice them when they were looking around for help. Sometimes I even started having fun, humming along to the cheery pop songs the store's radio station blared out 24/7. My own taste in music couldn't be more different, which sometimes led to real suffering on my part. There are only so many times you can listen to a song by One Direction. The constant radio had something to do with employee motivation, but the only effect I ever witnessed it having on the staff was selective hearing. It's easy to claim you can't hear your co-worker asking you for assistance when Taylor Swift is yelling at you to "Shake It Off."

So there I was, on autopilot, whistling softly and tucking in T-shirt sleeves, until that tug on my sleeve forced me to raise my head.

Every store has its regulars. But unlike, say, a coffee shop, where the worst a customer can do is spill their coffee, or take up space for half a day behind their MacBook, at KINGSwear, you couldn't ignore the regulars. They were the kind that required serious medical assistance—the psychological kind, I mean. Never mind that the staff was in no way prepared to handle those people—we also couldn't call security, and that was because KINGSwear didn't want to spend any money on security. They did, however, want to spend money on insurance against theft. I guess in the long run, that was cheaper than hiring actual people to prevent stealing.

Anyway, the woman standing next to me was our very own Crazy Cat Lady. She always looked like she had just escaped from the Calgary Zoo. Grey tufts of hair sprouted from her crinkly head. Her clothes, if you could call them that, were so full of holes and patched-up parts, it was impossible to tell what color they had originally been. Her bare feet were stuck in miraculously white flip-flops, as if she was usually walking around without shoes, and only put them on because she had to conform to what she thought of as a silly convention of human civilization. But by far the worst thing about her was her smell. She literally reeked like she took a bath in cat urine every day.

I immediately resorted to breathing through my mouth.

"You need some help?"

"I called you like three times already! Are you deaf, young man?"

I suppressed a sigh. Hopefully Marion, my manager, wasn't anywhere nearby to hear this exchange.

"I'm very sorry. How can I help you?"

"It's so hard to find good customer service these days. Nobody pays attention anymore in stores if you ask something."

No kidding. Maybe if good customer service included things like receiving respect and politeness from the customers, that would change.

"Again, I'm sorry. I didn't hear you the first time."

She ignored my repeated apology. "I need help finding something."

"What is it that you're looking for?"

"Oh, it's a standard item. This store should have several of them, but I can't seem to find any." She glanced around. "I'm looking for a pink sweater."

Here we go.

"I don't think we have pink sweaters."

"You do sell ladies' sweaters." It wasn't a question.

"We do. We just don't have them in pink. But there's this very nice white sweater that I could show—"

"I've been shopping here for over two decades. I always buy my pink sweaters here. There must be some in the back, I'm sure?"

No, there aren't. First of all because we don't sell pink sweaters, and second because 'the back' isn't some magical well from which I could pull your hypothetically existing sweater.

"I'm happy to go check for you, but I'm fairly certain we don't have them. Maybe you bought them at another store?"

"Are you saying I'm too senile to remember where I buy my sweaters?"

Deep inner groan.

"Ma'am, would you care to look at the other ladies' sweaters? Like I said, I'm pretty sure we don't have pink ones."

"I only wear pink sweaters. I'm absolutely certain that you carried them in this color the last time I was in here."

I imagined putting my hands around her neck and squeezing tight.

Liz Laidlaw

Finding Lotusland

In this historical fiction/mystery, a fourteen-year-old Vancouver Sun news-paper boy accidentally reveals a decades-old crime exposing the corruption of the city's development, putting his life in danger, while forcing him to discover more than he bargained for about his family's origins.

JULY 1972

CHAPTER 1: INCIDENT AT MARPOLE MIDDEN

Simon Pike realizes that he wanted to get caught. Something buried deep within him had enjoyed the experience of being involved in in-creasingly dangerous and questionable acts. There was a certain thrill, a cachet. An elevated status even. His father would be angry, sure, but his brothers, they might actually respect him for it.

But then the truth sinks in, and the urge to get away with it, or to get help even, overwhelms him. He rationalizes, revises, and excises certain events and actions, so that at one point he has convinced himself that it isn't him, it really isn't actually Simon who has done the dirty deed.

Innocent bystander. Victim, even.

And then he is sick to his stomach again.

His father, who has already disowned him, will not sympathize with any of it. And Simon's brothers, although their own activities are barely legal most of the time, have higher expectations of him. Who knew he'd be longing for the days when he was the most honest and upright mem-ber of the Pike family?

This part of the Marpole Midden by the shore of the Fraser River has always been the place Simon comes to. The pilings from the old

Marpole Bridge sit low and heavy in the water, a new on-ramp is rising to the west as part of the Arthur Laing Bridge, and the sawmill squats to the east. Always trying to stay on the right side of his father and his brothers at home is exhausting. The brush behind the Fraser Arms Hotel, where most nights his father can be found after working at the mill, is where Simon feels closest to peace.

Simon moves away from the pile of bones, wipes the sweat off his upper lip with the back of his hand, slaps at a few mosquitos, then comes closer again, and begins circling, looking at the chest from different angles. He is reluctant to touch the box. At least two bodies there, he thinks. He can clearly see two skulls, and what used to be two complete rib cages collapsed down on themselves. Any clothing has mostly disintegrated.

The box that he has pried open contains the bodies of two small beings. Their jawbones are so delicate, the teeth like mini-peppermint Chiclets. Their bones are not nearly as old as the other bits and pieces of bone and stone and shells scattered around the dirt and along the banks of the river. Those pieces, and this place, he knows from his Grade 8 Social Studies class, have been here even before Vancouver was here— the city before the city.

He never should have brought them here. Now he has ruined it— quite possibly forever.

CHAPTER 2: MYRNA

Looking at the broken box and the fragile bones makes Simon think of his mother, when she was still alive. She caught him stealing money from her purse. He'd been about six. It was Miles who put him up to it. Or maybe it was Eric. They'd wanted to go to the corner store for candy, and their mother had said no. The boys had begged, but she'd been adamant. Then the phone rang. Myrna gave the boys a look, lit a cigarette, and went to answer it.

The yellow rotary phone was on a wall in the kitchen beside the back door and Myrna looked out the screen door window into the scrubby backyard while she talked. She twisted the cluster of dirty plastic curls that was the phone cord around her fingers while she talked, cradling the receiver between her shoulder and her ear at an awkward angle.

Simon never felt like he fit in with his brothers, and he always wanted to please them. They were as different as chalk and cheese, Myrna said. Simon thought it more like he was stick and they were stone—he was tall and lanky with eyes to the distance most of the time, even as a baby. The boys were stocky and solid, always moved close to the ground. Miles, or Eric, nudged Simon towards their mother's purse, which sat on the hall table. Simon stumbled forward, looking back at his big brothers. They must have been teenagers then—big-footed, square-jawed, almost men, thickset and dark-eyed in contrast to Simon's slight frame, pale eyes, and long black lashes. He looked between his mother, talking on the phone, and his brothers around the corner, smiling and waving him on, and stuck his hand into his mother's purse, grasping the soft heavy wallet. Miles and Eric were ecstatic, silently cheering and punching the air. Simon started to move towards them, walking backwards, his eyes never leaving the back of his mother's head. Just then she turned around to find the ashtray, and her eyes caught Simon's. She had been smiling and was animated, clearly enjoying talking to whoever was on the other end of the phone.

Simon didn't remember his mother having many friends. Those she did have were from the church. Myrna ground out her cigarette in the little brown glass ashtray that overflowed on the kitchen counter and looked at her youngest son like she'd never seen him before. Simon knew she'd hoped for more from him.

The cancer was already eating away at her, and her face was almost hollow. Her clavicles stuck out so far it looked like you could hook a shirt hanger on them. As she blew out the smoke, the skin on her face started to fall. It fell like the support or structure had left it. Like all the life had gone out of it.

It was one of Simon's last memories of his mother, and he would forever wish that it was not her last memory of him. The phone conversation forgotten, Myrna whispered hoarsely, "Simon!" and Simon dropped the fat wallet and turned to run. His brothers' footsteps trampled down the wooden front steps of the house. He started to go after them, but Myrna, still surprisingly strong despite her condition, caught him by the back of his shirt.

CHAPTER 3: BY THE BANK OF THE FRASER

Simon looks out at the glassy surface of the Fraser. It is calm as it drifts by, but he knows the swirls on top mean there are strong currents underneath that can carry a body swiftly out to sea. He learned in school last year that the river is the longest in British Columbia, comes all the way from Mount Robson, and carries with it tons of sediment that is spewed into the ocean. He learned from his brother the Hul'qumi'num name for it—the Sto:lo. He thinks about what the river must see on its journey from the north as it cuts deeper and deeper into the Fraser Plateau and eventually forms the great Fraser Canyon. He has seen pictures in his textbook of Hells Gate where the canyon narrows dramatically and the entire volume of the river is forced through a narrow gap of only a hundred feet. Watching the river always makes him feel at ease, puts things in perspective somehow. What happens to him and what he does is inconsequential when compared to the power and enormity of the river.

Except for right now.

Simon turns back to the broken bentwood box. It is made of one continuous piece of red cedar. Even though the bottom corner of the large rectangular box has been smashed, like it has been dropped, he can see that it was beautiful. Someone took a great deal of time creating it. On the long side, there is the pale image of a moon with a face. It looks like a woman. And she is crying.

He can't bear to leave it as it is, exposed. But he can't stand to do what he has been asked to do either. Preparing to get the lid back on, he pushes the sides of the box together, and notices a silver button nestled among the bones. It is shaped like a maple leaf and stamped with a crown, the word POLICE in a scrolling banner along the bottom. He looks behind him, sensing someone is watching. Seeing no one, he pockets the button, picks up the smooth heavy lid and drops it back in place on top.

Using his pocketknife, he cuts branches of Scotch broom and arranges them around the box, sticking the stalks right into the rough sandy soil so that it is camouflaged and completely hidden. The yellow and brown flowers have already burst open and seeds spill as he works. Simon orbits the box one more time, making a few adjustments to cover it up, and mops the sweat from his face with the front of his T-shirt.

He glances at his watch, a Timex he's earned for selling the most new subscriptions to The Vancouver Sun over three months in the spring. He remembers how excited he was to win it, and shakes his head. It is impossible to reconcile how much things have changed in a few short months. The watch face says 2:10 pm. He has just over an hour before he needs to be at the newspaper shack to do his route and he has deposits to make at Pacific Press on the way.

Scanning the area one more time to see if there's anyone watching, he walks up the slope of the bank to where he's left his bike. He'll stop at home first for his newspaper bags. That's the logical place most people would go for help. For him, going home will be a waste of time.

Jennifer F. Santucci
The Camphor Tree

This excerpt is from Chapter One of "The Lost Daughter of the Forest."
It is about the journey of self-discovery and empowerment of Vivian,
a seventeen-year-old girl from an island nation filled with forgotten spiritual
magic. In this excerpt, Vivian bids farewell before beginning her journey.

Vivian opened her eyes, prepared for practice. She gripped her *kali* sticks, swung them in a forward windmill rotation to loosen her wrists and then swung them in reverse. The warmth in her body, mixed with the steady energy of the forest, created a singular focus on her body's movement. Her motions were no longer a thought, but a reaction to an imaginary opponent.

A bead of sweat trailed down her back between her shoulders, but the cool air under the tree was invigorating and so she pushed herself. She imagined that she was like the bamboo trees that lined the boundary of their farm-flexible in the wind, but strong when the wind and rain combined their forces.

Her sticks stopped in mid-air, when she felt it—a warning. For a moment, Vivian thought of her family and almost ran back home, but her legs stayed planted on the ground. Uliteg, her uncle, taught her that although he trained her to fight, she must not look for conflict. The tree's whispered meditative conversation with the leaves and wind had stopped—the forest was mostly quiet—mostly.

Careful steps made their way toward her. She could hear the small shake of the tall grass, as if one of the pythons of the forest were making its way to its prey. It was almost imperceptible, except that in the silence of the forest, the sound was clear to her. Not very far because the warning in the air became thicker. Her feet moved into a fighting stance, she tucked her chin down, and held her kali sticks at the ready.

Uliteg's imposing figure emerged from a cropping of tall grass. Tattoos on his arms and chest announced his fierce warrior reputation. If he weren't her uncle and mentor, she may have quailed at the sight of him. He was in his fortieth year, his dark brown skin was smooth, and the muscles of his biceps and thighs showed he was capable of great strength. His warrior's knot at the crown of his head was black with no hint of grey.

Sometimes, when they went to the market together, they would be mistaken for brothers. Vivian knew it was a compliment and that her true identity was safe, but she wondered what others would think if they found out she was actually his niece.

In Uliteg's hand was a short curved blade, the *karambit*. Uliteg's dark eyes darted to the camphor tree and then back at her. His guarded expression was meant to intimidate her, but instead it strengthened her determination. Vivian gripped the kali sticks and prepared to fight her uncle.

He stalked toward her, but Vivian circled away. His demeanor told her that this was a test. She did not know what the test was for, but she also did not want to disappoint him.

She would stop short of killing him.

Uliteg swiped his knife at Vivian's throat. She pulled back, but not before the rush of air from the karambit fluttered across her skin. It was a phantom warning that this test would have deadly consequences if she did not pass. They circled each other for a moment before he began to attack her in earnest.

The strike of Uliteg's karambit on her kali sticks sent small vibrations through her arms and shoulders. Vivian countered his moves with combinations of blocks and hits. Their fighting began to follow a rhythm of hit, block, sidestep, and swing. The energy of the tree and forest flowed through her, making her swings and jabs smooth and precise. She had not realized how hard they were fighting until she heard her uncle's labored breath and saw beads of sweat roll down his temples.

It was time to end this fight.

She followed up with a swing toward his temple, but he ducked and drew his knife out across her chest. He managed to slash her shirt, but she stepped back before the knife could do any further damage.

Her kali sticks rained on him. Uliteg dodged his head away from the high swings, but when her kali sticks swung low, they landed first on his knee and then at his shin. He let out a grunt and then lunged with his knife, attempting to slice her arm.

Vivian crossed her sticks and caught his arm instead. She twisted the sticks, causing the knife to fall away from Uliteg's hand. Then she hooked one stick under his knee and swept it away. Uliteg landed on his back, but twisted away before Vivian could land the final blow. She stabbed at him with one stick, but he rolled away again. She pursued him as he continued to roll, but he was quick.

A glint of metal caught her eye and she realized her uncle was rolling toward his knife. She sheathed her kali sticks in the holsters worn on her back, tumbled into a handspring and managed to get her uncle's knife. Before he could jump up, she held the knife at his throat.

"Inang is not going to like what you did to my shirt," she said.

Uliteg blinked, his expression less severe. "She will understand."

Vivian doubted her mother would understand. "Will you mend it then?"

His eyes softened and his good humor seeped into his expression. "No, you need the practice."

She stood up to give him room to stand. "I'd rather clean out the pig pen."

He laughed and then nodded. "You clean out the pig pen and I'll mend your shirt."

She was about to agree when she realized that the fence for the pen needed to be fixed, which would most likely lead to fixing the chicken coop too. "Never mind. I'll mend the shirt."

"Suit yourself, Vin."

She couldn't help smiling. He used her nickname when he was pleased after a sparring match.

Uliteg's eyes wandered over the camphor tree's massive trunk and up toward its jutting branches. "What would happen if you never saw this tree again?"

Vivian's face fell. "Why would you ask me that question?"

"We have a visitor." Vivian reached for her kali sticks, but Uliteg stopped her hand. "A friend of Apo's."

Her hand dropped to her side. Her grandfather hardly ever had visitors. She wanted to ask if this had to do with her father. She wanted to know if he had finally found them—found her.

She realized the answer to his question: they would have to leave if her father had found them, otherwise they would die.

Instead, Uliteg said, "Ask for blessings from the tree before you return home, but be quick. The visitor wants to meet you." He turned to the tree and bowed his head before returning home.

Once he disappeared into the forest, Vivian's throat knotted. The possibility that this would be the last time she would see this tree tore at her and a tear escaped.

She dropped to her knees and sat. She recited the ancient words that Apo had taught her and that acknowledged the tree as a living symbol of strength and serenity. The wind swayed the leaves and branches above her in an attempt to whisper reassurances. She bowed her head and closed her eyes to let the sound of the tree's chattering leaves wash over her. She realized then why she was driven to come to the forest this morning and why paths to other parts of the forest were blocked except for the one here and to the pond.

The camphor tree was saying goodbye.

It seemed like a ridiculous notion, but in her heart, she felt it to be true. Vivian opened her eyes. Blurred by tears, the image of the forest floor appeared. In front of her, the camphor tree had left it seeds. Her tears dried up and she looked up at the tree. The creak of the branches acknowledged her silent question. Apo told her never to take from the forest unless it was offered. She had listened to his warning, but this time, there was no doubt—she was supposed to take some of its seeds with her.

The idea that she could carry a part of this tree with her wherever she went gave her great comfort.

Vivian gathered five of the small brown sphere-shaped seeds and held them in her fist. She stood and with her empty hand she pressed her palm onto the bark of the tree. She wanted to remember the feel of the deep rough grooves that were etched on its surface. The groaning of the branches overhead reminded her that a visitor waited for her. She nodded and without further delay, returned home.

Leslie Comrie

These Are the Things That Change You

FOUR EXCERPTS FROM A NOVEL IN PROGRESS

Cecelia Margherita's world shifted dramatically with the arrival of Pierpaolo Pascolini.

Cecelia Margherita Miller, an architect by trade, was born in the restored ruins of the Fiesole Roman amphitheater and flung into the quaking arms of her father, Charlie Miller, a scant two minutes before the Italian ambulance screeched up the hill and screamed to a halt to assist with her precipitous birth.

Cecelia was in the final stages of saying goodbye to her first lover, Captain Fauconberg, a French exchange architecture student who loved her sweetly and suffocatingly without end. As she waved goodbye to what might prove to be the world's loveliest guy, a piece of her heart—a small, very small piece—attached itself to Captain's wake.

Cecelia met twenty-two-year-old Pierpaolo Michelangelo Bartholomeo Pascolini, Apollo-esque and born twelve days late in the circular ruins of the Roman Colosseum, quite coincidentally, on the edge of a blindingly sunny day. She tripped over Pierpaulo on her eighteenth birthday as he flew into her periphery, sliding headfirst along the asphalt of Cecelia Margherita's Toronto landscape, arriving on the good grace of his elbow and clutching the brake handle of his beloved Aprilla, landing full stop, his lips finally pressed against the tips of Cecelia's toes.

Pierpaulo landed dramatically at her feet like a replacement part sent by the Universe.

There were those that whispered to one another that Avalon Field wasn't born but hatched. How so-called intelligent folks could succumb to such a ridiculous thought made a person wonder, but to their credit Avalon's smallness and his condor-shaped nose gave him the look of something both bird-like and other-worldly.

Avalon, the eleventh of twelve children, was born smack dab in the middle of Iztapalapa, Mexico City. The moment Avalon took his first small gasp and cried out from between his mother's legs, the neighbour, Juan Alvarez, was screaming at his cousin who had driven his motorcycle headlong into and across the hood of Juan's brand new Mercedes, Avalon's father was sitting on a chair in his mistress Jacinta's kitchen, sipping coffee, Jacinta was brushing the dust from her knees and wiping the seed of the impatient father-to-be from her lips, and, marvelously and across the border, Rothschild Swift, a three-year-old thoroughbred bay gelding, was crossing the finish line at the Kentucky Derby in nearly the fastest time in history.

In some corners of his universe, it was whispered, Avalon was found in a basket floating down a river like Moses, and in others, Avalon dropped straight out of the sky like an asteroid hitting the earth, but Avalon's father, Carlos, a regular at the Plaza Mexico and the Hippodrome, believed his speedy birth was magically aligned to the Derby winner and a mano-a-mano champion named Francisco Monticello. Carlos overrode the exhausted newborn's mother's decision to call the infant Hector Joseph Carlos Diego Velasquez, and bestowed upon him the name of Avalon Rothschild Swift Monticello, the name of the jockey, the horse and the torero, combined.

Cecelia Margarita's sister, Charlie Bonneville, the unlikely wife of a middle-aged Neapolitan Duke, wandered around her spacious back garden, her short blond hair wet and clinging to the nape of her neck. The wings of a wasp brushed against her knuckles, and Charlie's hands shimmered in the noonday heat. The scent of lemon mint crushed between her fingers wafted up from the fading lyrics ballpoint inked on her palms.

Charlie, in the midsummer of her fifteenth year, uploaded a song to MySpace, one she'd written and recorded with her friend Avalon in her pale pink ensuite bathroom of their father's modest home in the Beaches of Toronto, and the song, a ballad-rap-sonnet about driving at night with boys through the sidestreets of Buffalo in a stolen car and shooting up snowmen, was interpreted by an online music magazine as a "fucking brilliant," "minimalist," narco-gangster-coke-rap tune, and naturally, the song went viral. By November, her first four-song EP was produced by a famous New York record producer in his Topanga Canyon backyard studio and by spring, Charlie was taking the music awards by storm.

By summer she was holding hands with particle physicists and Hollywood A-listers, and she found herself on the invite list to the front row of everything Ted, red, and force-fed. On the day she turned sixteen, she celebrated topless on an Ibiza beach with a well-known Hollywood director, her small ankles running from the ripples of the surging sea and the director's large hands wrapped around her small hips while her fifteen-year-old smile of yesterday was still wet upon his forty-seven-year-old lips.

By the time she was eighteen, Charlie was engaged to the aforementioned Italian Duke, whom Charlie had one evening mistaken for a server while dining with the film director at Pier Luigi in Rome. Utterly entranced by Charlie, The Duke, a poet by trade and thirty-six years her senior, had unearthed, in less than a day of setting eyes on her, that the thing she missed most in life was her off-the-track, retired four-year-old race horse, These Are the Things That Change You. Charlie received a delightful note from the mysterious Duke's assistant that her horse would arrive via FedEx within the week.

The Duke hand-walked her horse to the door of her rented Villa outside Rome, and by the end of her nineteenth summer, Charlie's former life had disappeared and she was now the wife of the middle-aged adoring Duke, living a quiet life riding These Are The Things That Change You, through the Neapolitan countryside.

⌒

Avalon Field left his adopted family and his divided heart when he was eighteen. He hopped a bus out of town, past the population sign of a city that had failed to reshape his otherworldliness. Avalon set out to hitchhike south with his constant companion, Sears Loyola.

Avalon and Sears, their thumbs dragging in the wind by the side of the road, took a ride in a beat-up two-tone brown Ford pickup truck, the owner of which slowed almost to a stop but kept moving on account he was pulling a double length horse trailer filled with a quartet of two-year-old horses. Avalon and Sears hopped into the open door, Sears going first as Avalon was the more agile of the two, and as soon as the door closed the driver accelerated towards their future, a capital-D Destiny at the Del Mar Racetrack.

Sears felt a paternal affection for the small and sweet Avalon that even Sears couldn't quite explain. The owner of the truck, short and fat, stinking like underarm and ass sweat and cigarettes, sat on a telephone book, and Avalon's small feet swung back and forth above the floor of the passenger seat. Though the larger of the two by far, Sears sat, his knees tucked up beneath his chin, on the bench seat behind the front to keep an eye on Avalon and make sure the owner of this truck—unlike the handsy-weaselly owner of the shiny blue Camaro that carried them a half mile earlier—would keep his hands to himself.

Despite the words Dave's Horse Trailering emblazoned across both sides of the truck, Avalon and Sears bestowed the cognomen of "Yep" to the pickup truck driver after he'd used the expression more than a dozen times in the first twenty minutes.

"You ever ridden a horse?" Yep asked Avalon, slowing and pulling the truck slowly to the side of the road. "No sir," Avalon said, shaking his head.

"Come on," Yep said. "Both of ye. Gimme a hand. You boys can earn your way west." Avalon pushed hard on the truck door and shivered as the wind passed straight through his jacket. The grass in the fields went flat and sat up straight to attention after the gust dissipated.

When the boys reached the back of the truck, the door to the trailer was open, and Yep had a huge, shining creature in hand. He passed a lead rope over the horse's neck and clipped it to a halter bound around the most beautiful creature Avalon had ever seen. Yep passed the rope to Sears, who balked at the size of the creature, his fear making the horse step high and spin its hind end around. Avalon stepped forward and calmly took the rope from Sears. He looked deep into the faraway eye of the animal as it lowered its head near enough to the ground for small Avalon to stroke the star on its broad forehead.

"Looks like you've got the touch son," Yep nodded, as he took his cap off his head, smoothed his hair and put it back on again. "Take, These Are the Things that Change You, for a walk and then let her graze for ten minutes. Not a second more, mind." Yep turned to Sears. "You grab the bucket and muck out that trailer son. We leave in thirty minutes."

Avalon, back in the truck, felt a thrumming in his entire body like he'd never felt before. He grew an inch in the second he stared into the universe of that horse's mind. The feeling Avalon exchanged with this exquisite creature sealed his divided heart back into a whole thing and left it beating like one of those primitive drums that call people back home at the end of the day.

Michel Beaudry

Storm Crossing

AN EXCERPT

The phosphorescence in the water is too beautiful for words. Especially in the dark like this. Katie watches the lightning squiggles of thousands of tiny fish as they scurry away from the boat. It's like viewing aquatic fireworks. Explosions of light in every direction. Behind them, *Bertha*'s wake cuts a silver furrow through the bay.

They've reached the mouth of the harbour now and Katie can see the flecks of neon white proliferating in the distance. She knows every fleck is a breaking wave. She feels the first drops of rain. And a trickle of adrenalin tickles her tummy. She turns to her uncle. "Looks pretty stormy out there," she says. "We can handle this ... right?"

"Of course we can." Her Uncle Dan looks so solid standing there at the wheel that it gives her a new blast of confidence. He smiles reassuringly. "It's like I figured, Katie. We're going to be in a following sea all the way to the island." He shrugs. "And you know what that means: we're just going to have to show those big ol' waves how well *Bertha* can surf."

His words are barely out of his mouth when the first swell of the journey has them in its grasp.

It feels strange to be lifted like that in the dark. Katie can sense the wave sweeping under *Bertha*, but she can't see it. It's like an invisible hand has taken hold of the boat and is slowly pulling it backwards. She feels a surge of nausea flow through her body. Feels the kick of the motor as her uncle coaxes *Bertha* to catch the colossus before it crests and breaks over them.

But will he succeed? The motor howls in protest. *Bertha* fights for purchase. But the wave keeps building. Bigger. Bigger. Bigger still. The phosphorescence is blasting bouquets of light all around them now. The wind is raging. A hard rain plinks off the deck. Katie watches it all with growing concern. The boat is going too slow. She's convinced of it. They'll never catch the wave going this slow. They'll never …

And then they're surfing. And everything goes still. There's a sense of quiet power that comes over a boat when it starts to surf. And Katie knows that; she's felt it before. But this is different. Tonight Katie feels the wave's wild will to the depths of her soul. And she sits in the first mate's chair, near-mesmerized, as her skipper plays off each swell to maximum advantage.

But she knows she's got a job to do too. She knows that a storm like this can create all sorts of hazards in the water: rogue logs from busted booms and forest blowdowns flushed into the ocean. Even bits of broken dock come unhinged from their moorings.

So she concentrates on the sea. Does her best to make out the hazards ahead of the boat. But it's tough going. And she worries that she might miss something. It's hard. So hard. But it's exciting too. And her courage grows as her eyes adjust to the murky glow of *Bertha's* spotlight. She's slowly getting the hang of it now.

The deadhead must have been waiting for them in the trough of a wave. A mariner's worst nightmare. This one is floating just below the surface. And Katie has no chance of seeing it.

Bertha smacks the big deadhead almost square on, at top speed. It feels like the boat just hit a brick wall. One moment they're slipping effortlessly down the wave like they've already done dozens of times, the next Katie is lying in a pool of water on the foredeck, a gash across her cheek and no idea what happened or how she got there.

She watches, in a fog, as her uncle comes rushing out of the wheelhouse with a life jacket in his hand. His eyes are wild. His mouth is grim. Katie can feel the boat listing dangerously now. How long has she been lying there? The wind is still howling through the rigging; the rain is coming down even harder. Katie watches, curious, as her uncle comes straight toward her. What is he doing? He bends over, scoops her under his arm, takes two steps sideways, grabs the windward rail with his other hand … and leaps into the water.

The shock of it takes her breath away. And then the pain comes: hard, intense, so deep inside her body that she thinks she's going to faint. She screams. And when that doesn't change anything, she screams even louder. Clings to her uncle like she's never clung to anything before. She feels the power of his arm around her. Feels his strength as he strokes away from the boat. Hard, like he's trying to escape from something. But where are they going?

She hears gurgling. Watery mutterings. The last unhappy chug of a drowning motor. And looks back just in time to watch *Bertha* begin to sink, see-sawing from bow to stern and stern to bow … slowly, slowly. Then *woosh*, completely gone. Katie can't believe how quickly it all happened. She begins to cry.

"Easy, easy," her uncle croons into her ear. And brushes his lips against her brow. "I know this is a scary time. But we're still together, Old Girl. Don't worry. I'll get you home."

Katie doesn't remember much of the next few hours. All she recalls is feeling desperately cold and wet and sad and uncomfortable. At some point in the night, her uncle wraps her up in the second life vest—"to keep you better insulated against the cold," he explains—and helps her climb onto his back so he can pull her through the water more efficiently. "Just like a baby seal does with her mom," he says. "That way we'll get to the beach even faster." And then he surprises her: "Would you like me to tell you a story?"

Katie has never been more miserable. "A story, Uncle Dan? Now?"

"Of course," he says. And smiles. "You know, a story. As in, once upon a time, on an island far, far out in the Pacific, lived a little girl named Katie who loved to play and swim in the ocean."

282

"Just like me, eh?" It's still dark. The waves are all jumbly now, but Katie can feel that her uncle has found a good swimming rhythm. They aren't moving fast, but they're moving.

"Yep," he whispers, "just like you. Well, one morning, *this* Island Katie decided to go for a swim at her favourite beach."

Katie is dead tired. Completely played out. All she wants to do is sleep. But the story … "So what happened, Uncle Dan?"

"For some reason," he starts, "on this day she decided to go swimming much further out than she'd ever gone before. But Katie didn't realize how strong the offshore currents were. And little by little, slowly but surely, our young friend was dragged out into the main channel by the island's fierce tides."

"Oh no. That's terrible. So what did she do?"

"There was nothing she *could* do. If not for a young dolphin swimming nearby, a lonely little dolphin who'd lost his own family to an orca attack just a few days before, well, I don't know what might have happened to Island Katie."

And so the story is launched. It's all about the unlikely friendship between a solitary island girl and an orphaned dolphin. It's totally believable. Perfectly pitched. And the uncomfortable hours melt away in the telling of Dan's tale …

But Katie knows it couldn't have happened that way. She understands her uncle couldn't have been telling her stories while swimming in such rough waters.

She wakes up on the beach. Alone. She can feel the wet sand rubbing up against her skin. The weight of the waterlogged life jackets pinning her down. She wiggles her toes, then her fingers. Moves her head from side to side. Hmm. She must be alive.

Hard to describe how bright the colours are for Katie this morning. How clear the sounds. Even the smells: the tang of the sea air, the seaweed's maritime musk. It's like she's being allowed to discover the world all over again.

She stands up slowly. Sways. Refocuses on her surroundings. It feels so good to be back on solid ground again. Feels so good to be alive. They made it. So where is her uncle?

She scans the foreshore. Nothing. There are people further down the beach, hurrying toward her. But Dan's familiar form isn't among them. "Uncle Dan," she cries. "Hey, Uncle Dan. Where are you?"

Suddenly she's surrounded by all these strangers. And she's being hugged and kissed, and blankets and hot drinks are being proffered. And everything is way too loud. She tries to fight them for a while. But they're too strong, too insistent, and she's too tired. She can barely keep her eyes open anymore. So she lets them do their thing.

But in her mind she continues calling out his name. "Uncle Dan, Uncle Dan. Where are you?" Over and over and over again. "Dan. Dan. Dan …"

Christine Lai

Colour Beginnings

AN EXCERPT

30 October 1857

I can see him, as if he were before me, a dark shape silhouetted against the light. About ten years ago, I accompanied Turner to Margate, his preferred location for seascapes. On that beach, he used watercolour on damp, blue paper, mixing in the pigments while they were still wet, creating a kind of aquatic picture that shifted continually, intermingling the dreamlike vapors of the clouds with the vivid sun, which dyed the sea bright red. "Still needs a dash of yellow," I remember him saying, after which he dropped a dollop of Indian yellow at the centre of the setting sun.

We had already begun to pack up the equipment, when he suddenly turned to the darkening sky, reopened the paint box and added a blackish-red shape on the waves.

"A buoy?" I asked, though I cannot be entirely sure if I hadn't said "rock" instead.

"Is it?"

"Well, I'm asking you, Mr Turner."

"Make of it what you will," he then let out a series of grunts, which I always took to be a signal for me to stop asking questions.

"In any case, it is a very fine picture."

"Is it?" he grumbled. "Not my best. But I do not need anyone to like it." He rolled up the picture while the colours were still wet and went off, leaving the smell of pigments behind him.

The picture stayed in my mind for some time after that day in Margate, though I did not see it again until now. Like Turner's other sunset scenes, this watercolour is not as captivating as his pictures of blue. Turner's blue is never one unbroken mass of colour, but is composed of many layers of liquid hues that mingle and melt, expanding outward beyond the frames of the painting, the blue that marks distance and movement. I am deeply in love with *The Blue Rigi*. Blue mist once draped over the distant mountains, but the entire watercolour is now buried beneath black dust. Perhaps the palette of *The Blue Rigi* was closer to a pale lilac that dissolved into blue? Or is "cerulean" still the best word?

"Mr Ruskin," Turner once said to me. "Colour is colour."

⁓

15 November *1857*

The death of friendship, like many other forms of death, creeps up gradually, in the same manner as the fading of paper in the sunlight, so that the change in hues is barely visible from one day to the next.

The final phase of the decline of my friendship with Turner occurred the evening after we had supper at Griffith's, and I walked Turner back to the studio. He said he'd be damned if I didn't come in for some sherry. So I did. He gestured towards the sofa in a way that suggested he had something to say. There was a single tallow candle in the room, the smell of varnish permeated the air, and Turner's portly figure was silhouetted against the window and the lights outside.

"Mr Ruskin," he said, "I thank you for your book. That new one," he pointed towards the wall as if the book were shelved there.

"*Modern Painters*?" My tone was perhaps overly eager, for it was the first time Turner had mentioned the book.

"Hmmm," he replied, with a clearing of the throat. "There has been much talk, Mr Ruskin, of your writing. You've something of a voice, they say."

"Thank you, Mr Turner. I only meant to point out what I see as the truth expressed in your paintings. It might not be readily apparent to the unschooled eye, or to those who do not possess the love of nature."

"Hmmm," he mumbled as he began pacing in the room. "You know I do not like all that religious nonsense. Art is art, what more would you have?"

I laughed and sat up straight on the edge of the sofa. "Mr Turner, you know we disagree on such points. Perhaps it is best to leave it at that."

I hoped he would join me on the sofa, but instead, he began to pace even more erratically. "I mean to speak to you about the piece you showed me." At which point, he produced from his desk drawer the manuscript of a review I had drafted.

"Oh, I had quite forgotten about that," I said, which was not the truth.

"Yes, yes. Well, perhaps we should forget it all together, hmmm? I do not think you should publish this."

I was taken aback and finished the sherry in one gulp. "I see. What might be the problem? I thought it a fair assessment of the painting, a companion even."

Turner stopped in the middle of the room, and frantically flipped to a page, and began reading, in too loud a voice, a passage that I have never been able to reread since.

"I do not like it," he concluded.

"I'm confused, Mr Turner. Is that not an accurate description of the work? I felt I had conveyed the truth of your picture, just as you had conveyed the truth of nature."

"Hmmm. It is not that." He sat down in an armchair and drank his sherry. "It is your language, Mr Ruskin. Your language. It is inadequate."

At that word, my rage, hitherto contained, rose to the surface. It was not the first time he'd used the word. "Inadequate, Mr Turner? Surely you cannot mean that. *Modern Painters* seemed adequate enough to help the public understand your work a little better."

"That is just the thing, Mr Ruskin. I do not think they've understood anything. The language misleads, and that is not what I want. You're giving a definite meaning to the picture when there is none."

"You are mistaken, Mr Turner. It does not mislead. It illuminates."

Turner nodded. "That is true some of the time. But this passage here," he pointed again to the page, "I simply do not know what you mean."

"I mean to defend you!" I said, a little too forcefully.

Turner paused. "But I have never asked you to defend me, Mr Ruskin."

"I made your name." As soon as I pronounced those words, I regretted them.

Turner frowned at me with confusion at first, then a little sadness. "And I made yours."

I grabbed the sheets of paper from him, and went on my way. We did not see each other for a long while after that evening; I did not publish the piece. Some time after, I do not recall how long, I stopped by his studio concerning a Royal Academy matter—or, rather, that was my excuse—and found he was not in. The housekeeper let me in and asked me to wait, for Turner was to return shortly.

Left in the studio on my own—the same that I am now in—I wandered around, and stumbled upon what I, or anyone else, was never meant to see. There, partially tucked under a stack of drawings, were pictures I had noticed for the heaviness of their charcoal outlines. I pulled them out and held in my hands depictions of contorted bodies and lovers entangled in the pleasures of the night, with unspeakable things drawn with precision and detail, enlarged and rendered grotesque in parts. The scenes were handled with such care and truthfulness, like anything else by Turner, so that moans of pleasure seemed to emanate from the papers. My hands trembled and I nearly dropped the drawings. Everything in my learning and teachings pushed back against those images of blackened carnality. At the time, I took those pictures to be irrefutable proof that Turner had suffered moral collapse, and yet I had spent years defending him against accusations of such failures of the mind. It took strength to slip those papers back as they had been, before I quietly went out the door. I never mentioned the incident to Turner or to anyone else. I never told him I knew him to be capable of the most luminous landscapes and the basest scenes of hell.

When I received Turner's Bequest a few months ago, the memory of those carnal pictures and of that evening's disagreement had faded. Instead, my initial thoughts were of the way Turner's hands moved over the aquatic pictures that were his colour beginnings. Before the paper dried, he had time to change indigo to violet, time to add a disorderly flourish to indicate a ship, time to work a pattern to suggest the rolling breakers of an agitated sea.

I wish I could return to the seaside with Turner, to the sunset seen through the artist's gaze, and the boundless Turnerian sky, with its wispy cirri melting into radiant pools of colour and light. I wish I could take some of these pictures with me, to the sea, and allow them to continue changing, in their inexhaustible way, moving towards another half-revealed state of beauty.

In the fading light of the day I can barely see the movement of my pen over the page. Turner used his paintings to board up broken windows or plug up holes in the walls, but I still feel the draft. In the corner, there are canvases stuffed inside boxes weighed down by stacks of books. The swimming motes in the air settle gently on the canvases. Underneath the filthy skylight, the blackened corners of the paintings look even darker, as if they belonged to the evening sky outside. I will begin by wiping away the soot from these once brilliant seascapes and I will write my entries for the Inventory.

Contributors

FOREWORD

Raoul Fernandes' first collection of poems, *Transmitter and Receiver* (Nightwood Editions, 2015) won the Dorothy Livesay Award and the Debut-litzer Award in 2016 and was a finalist for the Gerald Lampert Memorial Award and the Canadian Authors Association Award for Poetry. He has been published in numerous literary journals and anthologies including the *Best Canadian Poetry 2015*. He lives in East Vancouver with his wife and son.

AUTHORS

Akem is a graduate of the 2015 Southbank Writer's Program and the 2016 Writer's Studio at Simon Fraser University, where she was mentored by Hiromi Goto. The story excerpt in *emerge 16* is from Chapter One of "The Shadow Key," an urban fantasy novel set in Vancouver, B.C. Akem also has a passion for art and has a Certificate in the Digital Arts; the *emerge 16* anthology showcases her winning cover art submission. Visit *akem.ca* to view her portfolio and to get in touch.

Quinn Anderson grew up in Ontario and Quebec, but transplanted herself to the West Coast a couple decades ago. She has explored many genres of writing including creative non-fiction, autobiography, short fiction, travel, and experimental writing. Currently, Quinn is enrolled in TWS: Poetry and Lyric Prose. She has poems published in *The New Quarterly* and several chapbooks. She draws inspiration from the ebb and flow of voice, the space in between, and the mystery of the writing life.

Natasha Barber (maiden name Huumo) is in a state of change—not a small change. Rather, she has finally had the blinders removed and is now witnessing the devastation of a tsunami that crashed into her life years ago, destroying everything she understood about her life and life in general (except for her positive outlook). The ripples of loss have opened her eyes to the notion of beginning life anew, which includes exploring a new career as a writer. (It pairs well with her introverted self.) All in all, she is curious to see what her future holds.

Michel Beaudry has spent most of his life roaming the world in search of great and unique stories to tell. He has eaten whale meat with Greenland Inuit, hiked above the clouds with Inca descendants, retraced the Silk Route with Kyrgyz nomads, and explored Morocco's hashish trail with Berber tribesmen. His award-winning tales have appeared in *GQ*, *Reader's Digest*, *Outside Magazine*, *Sports Illustrated*, *The Globe & Mail*, *Canadian Business*, *Equinox*, and dozens of other publications. His story of Whistler, *Against All Odds*, won The International Skiing History Association's Ullr Medal for Best Book of 2002.

Lindsay Beckett is a writer and teacher from Victoria, B.C. She leads creative writing workshops using the Amherst Writers and Artists method developed by Pat Schneider. Lindsay believes that every person is a writer and every writer deserves a safe environment in which to experiment, learn, and develop craft. Lindsay's work has been published in magazines and chapbooks. As a lifelong learner, she is currently enrolled in the Writer's Studio Online at Simon Fraser University. She lives in Victoria with her husband, Jeff, Alfie—a rescue mutt from Alabama, and William, their cat with half a tail. But that's another story.

Carolyn Bentley has worked as a costumer in film and television for the past twenty years. Prior to that, she wrote and performed stand-up comedy and theatre pieces. As a writer of creative non-fiction, she draws upon the predicaments and experiences in her life, prays to the god of humour, then takes a leap of faith. She's a graduate of UBC with a Bachelor in Physical Education and holds a Master of Arts in Theatre from Western Washington University.

Judy Bicep used to flirt with vampires and zombies until she discovered her true love—ghosts. Two truths and a spec fic about her: she teaches math to zombies, a friend once saw a ghost in her bathroom, and she just finished a 200-page manuscript about a dystopia set in a Vancouver daycare.

Christina Boschmann is a visual artist from Berlin who grew up in London, UK. She writes mostly narrative poetry and when not writing she can be found training jiu-jitsu in her garage or playing guitar. Her background as a portrait photographer often weaves itself into her writing, creating portraits of place, people, and memory. Cigarettes, scent, and death are recurring themes in her work. In her spare time, Christina travels and, when possible, spends her time swimming in the ocean. She hopes to move to the Caribbean one day.

Yaron Sidney Butterfield is a third-generation Vancouverite who grew up on the beautiful North Shore. As an SFU graduate with a BSc. in Biochemistry, a minor in Cultural Anthropology, and a Certificate of Liberal Arts, he has a wide range of interests and passions. Yaron has been a genome scientist at the BC Cancer Agency for sixteen years and has contributed to forty-eight publications—three as first author—in scientific journals. He writes book reviews for brain cancer patients and contributes stories to an online blog. He enjoys painting (yaronart.weebly.com), reading, writing, playing ice hockey, hiking, running, and cycling.

Katrine Cardew writes funny, raw, touching stories and songs about self-discovery, sexuality, and relationships. Her free-spirited upbringing, as well as her career as a tantric erotic masseuse, contribute to a unique perspective on these universal themes. Audiences have called her writing and her performances refreshing, titillating, and eye-opening. She is currently working on her memoir at the Writer's Studio.

Jackie L. Carmichael is a Canadian-American writer and former newspaper publisher whose work has appeared in *The Dallas Morning News*, the *Edmonton Sun, Entrepreneur Magazine*, and other publications. She taught journalism to youth at the Alberta Legislature and the University of Texas—Pan American. In the 2016 cohort of the Writers Studio at sfu, Jackie is workshopping a novel set in Tofino. She's also writing a play based on her grandfather's four years in the trenches of wwi. Jackie fosters Little Free Libraries on the west coast of Vancouver Island, and curates the Facebook site, "West Coast Reads."

Emma Cleary is from Liverpool and holds a PhD in Literature from Staffordshire University, where she taught English and Creative Writing. Her short fiction has appeared in *Lighthouse Literary Journal, Shooter Literary Magazine*, and *Best British Short Stories 2015*. She is a fiction reader for *The Indianola Review*, and lives and writes in Vancouver.

Nick Clewley is an after-hours writer and photographer who lives in Victoria. He loves everything written by David Mitchell and Margaret Atwood, and is doing his best to write a novel he hopes they (and many others) will read one day.

Leslie Comrie is an artist, writer, matador, mother, reader, administrator, walker, photographer, equestrienne, lover, magic mucker, sleeper, dreamer, driver, thoroughbred racer, designer, free diver, fast talker, dog walker, stargazer, listener, looker, thought mapper, traveller, and pilot.

Coranne Creswell is an artist, writer, and world traveller who divides her time between the North Pole of Vancouver Island and the South Pole of New Mexico. She is a recent graduate of the Writer's Studio at SFU, where she has been honing her fiction-writing skills. Coranne is currently working on her debut novel, "White Bones, Green Grass," as well as incubating a collection that couples her poetry and artwork. She is most happy when foraging for stories while road-tripping into unknown places.

Clara Cristofaro has been many things in her adult life, including a garbage sweeper, a seller of fine cheeses, and a cheerful bureaucrat. But underneath, and above all else, she has always been a writer. Working in fiction and creative non-fiction, she aims to dig into the corners of every room and pull out those tiny, unexamined pieces of our lives that deserve to be seen. She loves anthologies like she loves mixed nuts and is delighted to count *emerge 16* as her first print publication.

Donna May Cross is a farmer and businesswoman who lives near Kipling, Saskatchewan. She is mother to Benjamin, Lane, Hazel, and Emerson. Benjamin died of brain cancer in December, 2013, and inspires most of her writing, a lot of which is set in her valley pasture, a tributary of Pipestone Creek. She is currently working on a memoir/pilgrimage novel exploring her internal journey after her son's death. Also in the works is a young adult novel featuring all four of her children, written as a way for her children to be together again, and to help them through their grief.

Elaine Cross spent her formative years in rural Saskatchewan before tumbling through South Korea and England, and finally putting down roots on the West Coast. Her writing explores in-between and perimeter places, and she is keenly interested in the tension created by disparate ideas, and looking in from outside. She writes from Victoria, B.C.

Tara Cullis did her PhD in Comparative Literature, but spent her career working on conservation with indigenous groups around the world for the David Suzuki Foundation. A high-ranking native chief in a remote village on B.C.'s coast invited her along on the "seasonal round" of his community's food-gathering camps to write his biography. Spring was seaweed camp at Kiel; summer was fish-processing in the canneries; autumn took them to Old Town for high-bush cranberries and moose; winter meant food-gathering at Clams Town and feasts in Hartley Bay. Tara's book unites comparative literature with conservation, rounding the circle not just of the Chief's life, but of Tara's too.

Zoe J. Dagneault grew up in the fertile orchard village of Naramata, B.C. Her recent work is influenced by the birth of her daughter and the newness of motherhood. Zoe's exploration of failing societal structures has most recently revealed the inevitable beauty and decrepitude of flawed systems. Her work has been published in *The Maynard*. Zoe lives and writes in Vancouver.

Jacob Enns is grateful. After that, he is a storyteller, first to the riders of the transit system in Edmonton. After crossing the mountains for love, he now mostly tells his creations to his son Aidan—which his son really likes. Encouraged by the support for these early stories at Christianne's Lyceum of Literature and Art, and with urging from his life-mate Linda, he went on to hone his craft at the Writers Studio Online at Simon Fraser University. He is writing a lyrical prose memoir and a middle-reader book about a clan of shapeshifters.

Adriane Giberson is a wordsmith and an artist. A Montreal native, she moved to Vancouver by way of California and has been getting her feet wet in the Pacific Northwest since 2009. An alumni of Simon Fraser University's the Writer's Studio Online program, she is currently working on a collection of poetry and a novel (or two). Her artwork has been published in *Collaborative Art Journals and Shared Visions in Mixed Media*, by L.K. Ludwig (Quarry Books, 2009).

Jocelyne Gregory, an SFU and Capilano University graduate, began her writing career early with a chicken joke in a Canadian kids' magazine. At age six, Jocelyne was on screen in a Steven King horror movie and at nineteen, she met with the father of zombies, George A. Romero. Perhaps this had something to do with her love of horror and speculative fiction writing. After a painful rejection by a literary agent, Jocelyne climbed out of a tear-stained bathtub, swore vengeance, and determined she would write the stories she wanted to read.

Sara Hansen lives in Brentwood Bay, B.C. and relishes its mild weather and salty, ocean air. She lives with her three boys (married to one) and insists their pets must be female. When she is not writing, you'll find her in her art room or garden, but first and foremost spending time with her two sons. She would love to grow productive blueberry bushes and unblemished kale, but is successful in neither. So she is satisfied with being an avid baker, over-analyzer, Netflix watcher, amateur foodie, spider saviour, gadget devotee, horse lover, magazine addict, procrastinator, and coffee connoisseur.

Born and raised in the Rockies, **Carole Harmon**'s wilderness trail led to the poetry workshop, TWS 2016. She has explored nature through photography and collage. Now Carole writes as a creature ambassador with this proposal: From the point of view of ensemble, rather than conductor, let's know the wordless ones we live among, understand their melody as well as our chorus, and join the orchestra. Her previous works include hand-made artist books: "Unsung—words and images" and "Pool." In Banff, through her companies Altitude Publishing Ltd. and Harmon Gallery, Carole created, edited, and published books of Canadian photography and history in the 1980s through 2012.

Amelia Teresa Hirota is currently pursuing a certificate in creative writing from the Writer's Studio at Simon Fraser University. She is writing a memoir about the adoption of her son from Malaysia. Amelia is one of the few Americans to adopt a Muslim baby from Malaysia. It took over three years and a move to New Zealand to get American citizenship for her son. She writes about adoption, family, food, and travel on her blog. Afflicted by chronic wanderlust, she is addicted to buying one-way airline tickets. Her next countries to visit include Mongolia, Norway. and Sri Lanka.

Lakshmi Iyer is currently pursuing a certificate in creative writing from the Writer's Studio at Simon Fraser University. She blogs for *The Huffington Post*. She can be found online on Twitter @lakshgiri. Lakshmi is working on her first contemporary women's fiction, tentatively titled "Hindsight." A mother by adoption and biology, she resides with her husband and children in the US Northeast. On most days, she can be found by the stove serving up hot food. When she is not cooking, she recounts the mundane-ness of her life in startling detail on her blog at http://lgiyer.com/blog.

Ken Johns is a debut novelist. Originally from Victoria, he has always explored life through fiction. His passion for cinema took him to Toronto in the mid-eighties where he acquired an honours degree in film and video production at York University. His occupations through the subsequent decades have included house painter, men's wear salesman, school bus driver, movie extra, track and field coach, driving instructor, stage actor, operations manager, and express courier. He lives in Richmond and writes speculative fiction to feed his daily requirement for story.

C. Bruce Johnson has a diverse range of experience in the word business. He has worked as a travel writer, a magazine editor, and a book reviewer, and he currently manages a team of copy editors. That means he fears dangling modifiers as much as the existential threats to humanity he writes about in his speculative fiction. His writing also delves into the themes of memory, nostalgia, and the uncanny versus the mundane.

Since the age of twelve, writing has been a way for **Azmina Kassam** to tap into the vast realm of experiential data, organizing it into a coherent form and making sense of the information that is her life. Kassam's writing allows the meaning given to thoughts and ideas to ferment, so she may share her common humanity with others through words and stories. Kassam was born in Nairobi, Kenya and has lived in Vancouver, B.C. for over thirty years. She is presently enrolled in the Writer's Studio at Simon Fraser University. Her writing is poetic, has a mystical quality, and captures hints of the esoteric.

Sarah Katyi is a writer and business professional, originally from Spruce Grove, Alberta. She is passionate about travel, education, and holds a degree in Commerce. However, her first love has always been the art of storytelling. Sarah is currently pursuing an MFA in creative writing.

Jan Klimas is a scientist, artist, thinker, and writer. As a research fellow in medical schools at University College Dublin and the University of British Columbia in Vancouver, Canada, he studies ways to improve addiction medicine education for physicians. He started to write with the Thursdays Writing Collective in February, 2015.

Grace Konn was born and raised in Vancouver, B.C. and now resides in Port Coquitlam with her family. She is a graduate of the Southbank Writer's Program and recently, the Writer's Studio—both at SFU. She also holds a Master of Science degree and is currently working on her first, full-length novel—a young adult, science fiction romance story. Grace longs for the day when a family vacation means travelling to a galaxy far, far, away. There she'll sip on cosmic drinks while writing young adult sci-fi novels under the light of two moons.

Originally from Vancouver, **Christine Lai** lived in England for seven years where she earned a PhD in English Literature and published articles on Romanticism and literary representations of Regency London. Christine has been writing creatively since early 2015, and is currently working on short stories and a novel project, while collecting notes for a fictional biography of P. B. Shelley. In her writings, Christine is concerned with the place of art in the contemporary world and the consequences of human-made catastrophe.

Liz Laidlaw has been published in *Room Magazine, Ascent Aspirations*, and *Portal Magazine*, among others. She is a past winner of the Nanaimo Arts Council Short Fiction contest. As a columnist for *Relational Child & Youth Care Practice*, Liz has published over twenty non-fiction articles inspired by being a parent. She has a BA in Creative Writing from Vancouver Island University, and as a member of the the Writer's Studio Online (TWSO) 2016 cohort is working on a novel inspired by the remarkable city of Vancouver.

K.H. Lau is a novice in creative writing. She is exploring children's speculative fiction and dark themes (the psychological kind) in adult fiction. She is into all things magical, mystical, and fantastical—where everything is possible—without earthly constraints.

Eric Macnaughton has a PhD in Interdisciplinary Studies from the University of British Columbia. His research is in the area of mental illness and homelessness. After reading his prose, reviewers have speculated about the (unlikely) possibility that he is the illegitimate son of Joan Didion and Ernest Hemingway. He lives in Vancouver with his wife Catharine, their two sons, Ben and Oliver, and two guinea pigs.

Emmet Matheson grew up in Saskatchewan. He has written for newspapers, magazines, radio, TV, and the web. He lives in East Vancouver with his wife and three children.

Renée McTavish is a semi-reformed technical writer who put aside creating accounting software help to focus on writing speculative fiction. An Ontario native, Renée came to Vancouver in 2006 armed with a BA in English Literature, ready to explore life, the mountains, and everything. Renée is currently working on a novel-length portal fiction piece set in Vancouver and Garibaldi Provincial Park, as well as several short stories—a few of which are out and about hoping to catch the eye of various publications. Renée's excerpt piece in *emerge 16* is her first publication.

Lisa Milne is a lyrical prose writer who is finding her place in the Vancouver writing community, thanks to the Writer's Studio at SFU. Her strengths lie in unbound description and microscopic detail. Recently, she read her first Fred Wah and heard it described as biofiction: fragments of life embroidered and re-framed into narrative, fond of the ungrammatical and unending sentence. She is thrilled to now have a word for what she does. Lisa is a lifelong Vancouverite, night owl, and faithful devotee to the church of MacLeod's Books.

Sandi Myrlene is an author. She is in the process of writing a novel, "Frozen In Time." She has also written four children's books, and is writing a non-fiction book for childcare professionals. She has run a writing program for adults with mental health issues and has written tidbits of creative writing in their monthly newsletters. She completed a year long program in Professional Writing, with a focus on editing, through Grant MacEwan Community College. Her hobbies include singing, reading, scrapbooking, sewing, and quilting.

Emily Olsen is an emerging writer currently working on her debut novel, "Drifting in the Clouds." She is also writing a compilation of poetry and lyric prose about the richness of family and place, twin blessings in her life. Emily draws on her experiences of living in vibrant coastal communities in both New Zealand and Canada, where the arts and culture remain an integral part of life. Emily lives with her husband and two children in Brentwood Bay, B.C.

Loghan Paylor graduated from Concordia University's creative writing program, and has worked as a journalist, writing instructor, and theatre critic. Loghan lives in Abbotsford with their partner, two cats, and a mischievous husky dog.

Ivy Pharness is a writer of screenplays, short poems, and satirical short stories. She thoroughly enjoys the writing process when it is unencumbered by obsessive self-editing and doubting which, although helpful, can make her writing life trying, at best. Ivy enjoys biking in quiet residential neighborhoods devoid of traffic and eating like a starved animal when nobody is watching. She lives in Vancouver, B.C., with her houseplant and a handsome fellow with whom she shares a miraculous mutual attraction.

H.C. Phillips—that is, Hannah—thrives on the creation of poems, short stories, and novels. In particular, she looks to apply her critical mind to character-focused explorations of worlds and meaning. She lets a curiosity for new ideas ebb and flow in and out of her writing. She hopes to continue to explore the world of words and to see where this path takes her.

Helen Platts-Johnson is a recovering construction project manager turned author. She mainly writes contemporary young adult fiction, but occasionally strays into middle grade and fantasy. Her work has been awarded an honourable mention in the Writer's Digest Annual Writing Competition and several other "prizes" from her two mischievous cats.

Ben Ross is a retired general surgeon from South Langley who enjoys puttering around his hobby farm, shovelling horse manure, and reading poetry. He is married with three children and one very large dog.

Jennifer F. Santucci was an English teacher for over ten years and wrote fanfiction as a hobby when she wasn't teaching. During maternity leave for her fourth child, she (finally) realized writing was not a hobby. She is currently a stay-at-home mother by day and writer at night. Before the Writer's Studio, she completed certification in copy-editing and has also been trained in developmental editing. She is an avid reader, especially of young adult literature. She was born and raised in Southern California where she lives with her family. "The Lost Daughter of the Forest" is her first novel.

Jasmine Frances Sealy is a teller of lies on the internet. She writes mostly short fiction and when she rhymes it's usually by accident. Born in the United Kingdom and raised in Barbados, she moved to Toronto in 2008 and has been a recreant infiltrator and a semi-heretical observer of Canadian culture ever since. Her short story "Halved" was shortlisted for the Quebec Writer's Competition and her work can be read in the QWF Writer's Anthology 2014, as well as on her blog www.poetinside. com.

Cynthia Sharp had a fabulous year in the Writer's Studio. Her work has appeared in a number of literary journals and been nominated for the Pushcart Prize and *Best of the Net Anthology*. She enjoys the beauty of nature on the West Coast, where she is at work on her "Marcie of the Stars" fantasy series.

Over the last twenty years, **Jennifer Simon** has been an educator in Canada and the United States. Her adventurous journey to find true love brought her to Maple Ridge where she is now the principal of an elementary French Immersion community school. She enjoys getaways to the mountain community of Sun Peaks with her husband and five-year-old twin boys. Jennifer began writing to slow down and reflect on what she is curious about and has established a following with her blog: *Exploring What Is Possible.* Jennifer is currently working on a book about her experiences in schools.

Crystal Soto is of Aboriginal/Scottish descent and from Vancouver Island. She's an Island Girl at heart. Her mother is Tsimshian from Hartley Bay, her father—a street kid from Prince George. They both shaped her as a writer immensely. Her mother gave her a copy of Anne Rice's *Interview with the Vampire* at age eleven, which sparked her love of books. Crystal was raised on '80s horror movies, because her mother was too scared to watch them alone. *Star Trek, Star Wars* and the weird in-between brought her and her father together. She hopes to create similar stories that leave readers wondering, *what if?*

Sylvia Symons spent most of her childhood in the Hart Highway area north of Prince George. She now lives with her husband and sons in Vancouver where she teaches ESL at Langara College. Her work is published in *EVENT* magazine and is forthcoming in *Geist* and *Best Canadian Poetry, 2016* (Tightrope Books).

Lucía I. Terra has a background in social and cultural anthropology, languages, education, communication, and peace studies. After too many years of collecting degrees at universities around the world, she spent the past decade and a half based (mostly) in beautiful Vancouver, editing, translating, and writing non-fiction articles about cultural and social issues. She currently serves as the Greater Vancouver Regional Representative for the Federation of BC Writers and is trying to finish a memoir (in English) and a travel book (in Spanish).

Lisa Voisin is an author of young adult fiction, a technical writer, and a meditation teacher. She has published three books. Her debut YA fantasy novel, *The Watcher* (Inkspell 2013), won the Chanticleer Grand Prize for Paranormal fiction. Her third book, *The Warrior Prophet*, was released in April 2016. In her spare time, Lisa leads a writing group for teens with the Lynn Valley Literary Society. Though she's lived in several cities across Canada, she currently lives in North Vancouver with her fiancé and their adorable cat Popo.

Heather Louise Walmsley is an emerging writer of poetry, essays, and fiction. Raised in Yorkshire, she has worked as an EFL teacher, a journalist, a dialogue facilitator, and an environmental activist. She has an MA in Postcolonial Literature, a PhD in Sociology, and was recently a SSHRC Banting Postdoctoral Fellow at UBC, researching reproductive tourism in Mexico. Heather's poetic quest is to write into human fear and grief and amnesia, the shadow of rationality, and our mystical and sensual intimacies in nature. She is awed by surge of ocean, dreams of plants, and the joyful shrieks of her daughters.

Kitty Widjaja is a multicultural writer and visual artist who often tilts her head to the question: where are you from? She takes inspiration from Southeast and East Asian histories and culture in her works. Working in the realm of speculative fiction, she strives to bring fantastical elements into her stories that reflect the mythologies and lore she grew up with. She is currently working on a high fantasy novel as well as multiple short stories.

Martina Wolff has a degree in American Literature and currently works as an editor, translator, and teacher. Her fiction writing includes short stories, movie scripts, and her first novel, "Retail Kings." Born and raised in Germany, Martina has been calling Vancouver home since 2014.

Alessia Yaworsky has a Bachelor of Commerce in Marketing and a minor in English Literature from UBC. She has lived in Italy, South Africa, and Vancouver, and continues to enjoy exploring the far corners of the world (when not reading, writing, or discovering local hiking trails). Alessia is currently working on her first novel and a number of short stories, and is always looking for new sources of inspiration.

Production Credits

Publisher
Andrew Chesham

Managing Editor
Janet Fretter

Editorial Team
Section Editors
Nikki Hillman,
   Non-fiction Editor
Rebecca A. Coates, Speculative
   and YA Fiction Editor
Chelene Knight, Poetry and
   Lyric Prose Editor
Helen Polychronakos,
   Fiction Editor

Copy Editors
Christina Boschmann
Emma Cleary
Jasmine Sealy
Alessia Yaworsky

Production Team
Emily Stringer,
   Production Editor

Judy Bicep
Yaron Sidney Butterfield
Renée McTavish
Lucía I. Terra

Marketing Team
Katrine Cardew
Zoe Dagneault

Acknowledgments

The students of the Writer's Studio would like to thank their mentors for the guidance and insight they have provided. We also extend special thanks to the mentor apprentices for their support throughout the year.

We are grateful to Cottage Bistro (4770 Main Street) for graciously hosting our monthly reading series.

We would also like to thank John Whatley and SFU Publications for co-publishing this year's anthology. Their generous support enabled us to work with alumni and students in the production of *emerge 16*.

Thank you to Joanne Betzler and Grant Smith for their support. Their generosity allows us to make the *emerge* book launch a fun and lively event.

The Production Team would like to acknowledge that *emerge 16* was assembled on the traditional unceded territory of the Coast Salish people.

Year after year we are favoured by the support of independent bookstores who stock and sell *emerge*. We encourage our readers to return the favour by supporting local booksellers. A partial list of independent bookstores in Vancouver includes:

32 Books	The Paper Hound Bookshop
Banyen Books	People's Co-Op Bookstore
Book Warehouse	Pulpfiction Books
Hager Books	SFU Bookstore

Elzevir A*a* Q*q* R*r*

The interior of *emerge* is set in DTL Elzevir. Originally created in the 1660s, Elzevir is a baroque typeface, cut by Christoffel van Dijck in Amsterdam. As noted in Robert Bringhurst's *The Elements of Typographic Style*, baroque typography thrived in the seventeenth century and is known for its axis variations from one letter to the next. During this time, typographers started mixing roman and *italic on the same line*. The Dutch Type Library created a digital version in 1993 called DTL Elzevir. It retains some of the weight that Monotype Van Dijck, an earlier digital version, possessed in metal but had lost in its digital translation.

The interior of *emerge* is printed on Boise Polaris premium paper, produced by Boise Paper. The cover for *emerge* uses Kallima Coated Cover CIS paper, made by Tembec. Both papers are Forestry Stewardship Council (FSC) certified, and are acid free/elemental chlorine free.

emerge

AVAILABLE AS AN EBOOK

Since 2011, *emerge* has been available
in print and ebook editions.

Visit

amazon.com

and

kobobooks.com

for more details.